D1445813

Break of Day

and

The Blue Lantern

Break of Day

"Are you imagining, as you read
me, that I'm portraying myself?
Have patience: this is merely my model."

COLETTE

 ## *Break of Day*

TRANSLATED BY ENID MC LEOD

INTRODUCTION BY GLENWAY WESCOTT

and

The Blue Lantern

TRANSLATED BY ROGER SENHOUSE

Farrar, Straus and Giroux New York

INTRODUCTION

by GLENWAY WESCOTT

In the lifework of Colette, which is massive, though in small and simple forms—short novels and nouvelles and short stories and sketches and memoirs—*Break of Day* is especially meaningful and central. Central even in the way of paper and printer's ink, it is to be found in volume VIII of the *Oeuvres Complètes,* with seven octavo volumes before it and seven after it. In our understanding of her narrative art as a whole, it is impressive as a kind of divide or watershed, halfway between her storytelling and her vein of autobiographical subjectivity, and indeed between fact and fiction; halfway also in her life, between her unforgettable mother, Sido, and her exemplary final husband, Maurice Goudeket. Even her style in it is transitional and momentous, a matter of echoing, reminiscing effects, and of little clarion notes of surprise and prophecy here and there; befitting that time of life which has been called the old age of youth and the youth of old age, a time fraught with heartache and youthful tensions.

An almost careless admixture of autobiography in her various forms of fiction was characteristic of her even in her salad days, when her first husband, Willy, bullied her into writing, and she let him sign her books, temporarily: the series of five about Claudine, and the two about Minne, which she later re-made into one. Renée Néré, the heroine of *The Vagabond,* which established her reputation as a serious novelist—the sad divorcee bravely earning her living as a "modern" dancer in vaudeville—was obviously and avowedly a self-portrait. Upon occasion she mingled things the other way round, carrying elements of her yarn-spinning over into the early volumes of non-fiction: for example, the most important of her tributes to her mother is entitled *La Maison de Claudine,* as one might say, *The Home that Claudine Came From.*

In *Break of Day,* which is in story-form, nouvelle-form, the mingling is stranger than ever. It frankly purports to be an experience of her own, and she portrays herself not only in the throes of it but with pen in hand, fountain pen in sunburned, garden-hardened hand, all through the summer night and in the dawning blueness of another day, day after day, writing it. The name she gives herself in it is the same as on the title page: "Colette." Furthermore, she surrounds herself with known unfictitious friends: Carco, the successful novelist, Segonzac, the famous painter, Thérèse Dorny, a beloved comedienne of those days, and others. Only, evidently, Vial, a young man whom this "Colette" loves and decides not to go on loving, is fictitious.

Most nouvelles, which somehow take place in a perpetual, mobile present, with continuous up-dating of the past and continuous glimpsing of the future, have simple plots. What could be simpler than the plot of *Break of Day?* A literary woman in her fifties has been enjoying an amorous intimacy with a man in his thirties. Into the picture comes a strong young woman who has made up her mind to marry him. Thus far, he seems not to have fallen in love with the young woman; he still loves the older woman; but she is ashamed to compete, perhaps afraid to. She gives him up and sends him away, and resignedly dedicates herself to an independent way of life, with her good friends and beautiful cats, with her garden and orchard and vineyard, with her literary subject matter (including what has just happened) and her sense of style, decisive in morals and mores as well as in literature.

What necessitated this renunciation? That is suggested to us by the secondary sense of the title, *la Naissance du Jour:* the birth of the day, the coming of the light, revelation. In the pattern of her intimacy with the young man—altered, though only slightly altered, by the marriageable girl—it has been revealed to her that he will not be able to make her happy much longer; neither will any other young or youngish man. Worse still, it is going to be impossible for him to keep from making her unhappy. To suffer from ill-founded expectations of love at her age is beneath her dignity. It is her duty, she thinks, to avoid unhappiness of that order.

In his tender, distinguished memoir, *Close to Colette,* Maurice Goudeket assures us that Vial was not modeled upon him in any essential. Certainly, let us take his word for this, although the dates and overlapping circumstances to be noted in two recently published volumes of Colette's letters are striking and must have meaning. Colette and he first entered into a romantic intimacy in 1925 when they were aged, respectively, fifty-two and thirty-five. She wrote *Break of Day* in her house in Saint-Tropez, which is the scene of it, and in a hotel nearby in Provence (when Goudeket was in Paris), in the autumn of 1927 and the following winter.

We often thoughtlessly say that art takes a long time, whereas life is short, *Ars longa, vita brevis;* which saying seems to relieve the embarrassment of unenergetic artists, but is not necessarily true. In fact it may be quicker and easier to write a story than to love or hate, settle down or run away, marry or part. The creative faculty is able to do some experimenting with the creator's life, which may be to his or her advantage.

Certainly, for Colette, the renunciation of love accounted for in this fiction of "Colette" and Vial was, in actuality, the road not taken. Her loving companionship with Goudeket went on uninterruptedly; she refers to him in almost all her letters from 1925 on. In 1935 they got around to a formalization or legalization of their relationship, and he was her perfect helpmate, watchdog, adviser, editor, and (as she customarily called him) "best of friends," until her death in 1954. It is hard to think of Goudeket as ever having been a mere lover and beloved (like Vial), so greatly did he transcend that youthful role in the successive decades. He has not written boastfully of the transcendence; but pages and pages of her elderly autobiographical writing have a marvelous aura of appreciation of him. I do not see how she possibly could have accomplished the latter part of her lifework, while having to endure a martyrdom of arthritis, in demoralized, defeated, occupied France, had it not been for their marriage.

Thus we may conclude that *Break of Day* was a hypothesis which did not come true, and that Vial was a

personification. What she had to say farewell to was just
a part of herself, and just one aspect of love; the fierce
and fearful narcissism of always wanting to mirror oneself in the beloved, the weak possessiveness, the hopeless,
unnecessary jealousy, and the point of pride. Indeed it is
a wonderful simplification to be able to attribute all one's
happiness to someone, and to blame that same someone
for all one's unhappiness; but there are other simplifica-
tions for us as we grow older.

The word "love," in a love-story—and in almost any
criticism of fiction, unless the critic spells out his meaning—is apt to connote only that magic realm in which,
as Sir Thomas Browne has expressed it, two people "so
become one that they both become two." Perhaps there
is, or can be, some truth in this in young manhood and
young womanhood; certainly it grows false and fatal as
the years pass. Farewell to it, Colette said in this story;
never again! And if she had not exorcised and uprooted
the romanticism in herself by some such creative effort
as this broken-off romance with imaginary Vial, she
might not have had the courage to entrust the rest of her
life and her lifework, and indeed the glory after her
death, to Goudeket.

How much sadder the story is than the reality turned
out to be! Here we may see a disadvantage in the com-
bining of true personal materials with the composites and
embodiments of fiction. Knowing the rest of Colette's
life as she lived it, perhaps we cannot take the somber-
ness of the tale as literally as she intended. The implica-
tions are somber. Any piece of authorship that ends in
leavetaking and in the solitude of the one left behind

(though left behind to write, as in this case) touches upon everyone's loneliness and the universal anxiety. It reminds us of the one really hateful thing about life: that we must all depart from it eventually, or to state the matter more exactly, that it must depart from us, is departing from us.

But Colette's melancholy writing is saved from dreariness and desolation by her stoic sense. It is a somewhat nobler and, I may say, better-natured form of stoicism than the mere endurance of distress. Though she never jokes, there are gleams of humor, bitter mischief, and brilliancy, round and about her every sad saying and every poor prospect. Having said things or portrayed things, she rather simply forbids herself to be distressed by them any longer. She forces the distressing matter, disappointment or injustice or bad luck, all the way down inside herself, into depths of literature, profundities of love, and other almost mystic depositories of her thinking; and she gives us to understand, induces us to believe, that she is strong enough to be able to do this without too many of those cross-purposes of the mind and the nervous system which we call neuroses.

Break of Day begins with a letter from her mother, Sido, to her second husband, Henry de Jouvenel, declining an invitation to visit them in Paris, the year before her death; other maternal letters, in whole or in part, are interspersed in the text; and Colette handles a good many of her fictive incidents and arguments as it were in a musical composition, variations on themes of Sido's life and Sido's thought: notably, an intense responsiveness to physical beauty, which is not often characteristic of the female sex; fastidiousness and pride, especially with regard to the imperfections of the decline of life; and great work-morality. It makes a strange immortal atmosphere: a ghostly presence, handing down feminine ideas from generation to generation.

The reason Sido declined to visit Colette and Jouvenel was that a pink cactus which someone had given her was in bud. In untropical France, she explained, it was apt to blossom only every fourth year. If she missed it this time, she might not live to see another blossoming. This is on the first page, and on the second page, Colette imagines her mother's joyous concentration, with an enraptured expression smoothing all the wrinkles out of her old face, bending down and watching the place in the midst of the knife-edged plant where the promise of the flower was thrusting—"a woman who, like a flowering plant herself, had gone on indefatigably unfolding and opening for three-quarters of a century"—and on the third page, we have Colette's acknowledgement of the similarity of her own almost perverse, blissful gaze at her Vial as he slipped out of her bed, out of her house, at daybreak.

When Sido, in her mid-seventies, played chess with a little shopkeeper in her village, she kept on the alert for any sign of her senescence. "When I become too disgraceful and impotent at it, I shall renounce it as I have renounced other things, as a matter of decency."

In still another letter the solitary old woman, though in danger of fatal illness, objected absolutely to a family plan of hiring someone to spend the night in the house with her. No poor substitute companionship in the wee small hours for her! she protested, and itemized the miseries involved: the rumpled bed and the unpleasant toilet-bowl, alien inhalation and exhalation in the dark, and the humiliating prospect of having to wake up with someone else in the room. "Death is preferable," she said, "it is less improper."

No wonder that the daughter of such a woman minded the compulsions of love as she began to feel unyoung. Goudeket has told us that, even as an octogenarian, with every excuse of arthritic immobility and last-minute literary endeavor, his wife would not admit him to her room in the morning until the tasks and technicalities of her toilet and make-up and wardrobe had been completed.

Colette's father had also cherished a packet of letters written to him by Sido when she had been obliged to spend some time in a nursing home after an operation. After his death she found them all in his desk, and expressed a sort of disapproval. "What a pity that he loved me so much! It was his love for me that annihilated, one by one, the fine faculties that might have inclined him toward literature and science. He chose to keep dreaming of me instead, tormenting himself about me; and I found this inexcusable."

It is what I call work-morality. According to the idealism that the strong-spirited mother and the gifted emancipated daughter had in common, it is wrong to pride oneself on any mere greatness of love or mere intensity about it or mere continuation of it. Let us ask ourselves, instead, what results from it in the other areas of our lives, lifelong: perhaps a strengthening and steadying of the various functions of head and heart, perhaps not; possibly a tribute to it in some way, by means of intelligence and talent, or it may be, alas, nothing but inhibition and vapidity.

Break of Day is a story of literature as well as love. When Colette declared in it that she felt duty-bound not to subject herself to untimely, unnecessary unhappiness, the duty that she had in mind was her vocation of letters. "As of that date, the time had come for her to lay in a supply of her customary lifelong pale blue paper, to take pen in hand, to rediscover in her memory the great traces of nature and human nature, the pleasures and sorrows of the prime of life, and to convey them to others' minds, readers' minds, by means of well-focused language and logical grammar and clarifying syntax and sweet euphony; and never again to be distracted from literature by life. "Cold with emotion is the bronzed hand, which races upon the page, stops, crosses something out, and starts again; cold with a youthful emotion."

From that time on, pride and courage and vocation were to be the predominant moral concepts in her work, and pantheism was to be its principal emotion, transcending individual or intra-personal feelings. I find the imagery of nature-worship in *Break of Day,* even in English, enchanting. Turn the page now, and see for yourself: the ripening color of the Saint-Tropez afternoon, after the siesta, with a cat also rousing from its siesta, yawning like a flower; and then the descent of the North wind, the mistral, anesthetizing all that part of the earth between the Alps and the Mediterranean; the early morning seascape, blue-black, and scarcely awake yet, when Colette went wading out into it, then trudged back up the beach with a load of seaweed, to make a mulch around her tangerine-trees; the beautiful child holding a rose, on the threshold of Sido's sickroom, afraid of her because she was dying; even Vial's naked beauty—his body somehow more exact, more aroused, more expressive than his face—with antique patina of sunshine and salt water, and a bluish light shining on his shoulders, a greenish light girding his loins. Death and sex also subordinated to a general concept of the rightness of nature. . . .

If one is religious at all, in the pantheistic way, when the fateful farewell time comes, it may be easier to forfeit and to take leave of things beloved, things more or less perfect, at their peak—the pink cactus in bloom —than any lesser thing, worn away or overblown. In case of the more acute and tragic deprivation, one can at least keep, for remembrance and for a kind of worship, a god-like image, a concept of heaven on earth. So, at the time of writing *Break of Day,* Colette evidently thought.

"*Sir,*

"*You ask me to come and spend a week with you, which means I would be near my daughter, whom I adore. You who live with her know how rarely I see her, how much her presence delights me, and I'm touched that you should ask me to come and see her. All the same I'm not going to accept your kind invitation, for the time being at any rate. The reason is that my pink cactus is probably going to flower. It's a very rare plant I've been given, and I'm told that in our climate it flowers only once every four years. Now, I am already a very old woman, and if I went away when my pink cactus is about to flower, I am certain I shouldn't see it flower again.*

"*So I beg you, Sir, to accept my sincere thanks and my regrets, together with my kind regards.*"

This note, signed "*Sidonie Colette, née Landoy*", was written by my mother to one of my husbands, the second. A year later she died, at the age of seventy-seven.

Whenever I feel myself inferior to everything about me, threatened by my own mediocrity, frightened by the discovery that a muscle is losing its strength, a desire its power or a pain the keen edge of its bite, I can still hold up my head and say to myself: "I am the daughter of the woman who wrote that letter—that letter and so many more that I have kept. This one tells me in ten lines that at the age of seventy-six she was planning journeys and undertaking them, but that waiting for the possible bursting into bloom of a tropical flower held everything up and silenced even her heart, made for love. I am the daughter of a woman who, in a mean, close-fisted, confined little place, opened her village home to stray cats, tramps and pregnant servant-girls. I am the daughter of a woman who many a time, when she was in despair at not having enough money for others, ran through the wind-whipped snow to cry from door to door, at the houses of the rich, that a child had just been born in a poverty-stricken home to parents whose feeble, empty hands had no swaddling clothes for it. Let me not forget that I am the daughter of a woman who bent her head, trembling, between the blades of a cactus, her wrinkled face full of ecstasy over the promise of a flower, a woman who herself never ceased to flower, untiringly, during three quarters of a century."

Now that little by little I am beginning to age, and little by little taking on her likeness in the mirror, I wonder whether, if she were to return, she would recognise me for her daughter, in spite of the resemblance of our features. She might if she came back at break of day and found me up and alert in a sleeping world, awake as she used to be, and I often am, before everyone.

Before almost everyone, O my chaste, serene ghost! But you wouldn't find me in a blue apron with pockets full of grain for the fowls, nor with secateurs or a wooden pail. Up before almost everyone, but half-naked in a fluttering wrap hastily slipped on, standing at my door which had admitted a nightly visitor, my arms trembling with passion and shielding—let me hide myself for shame!—the shadow, the thin shadow of a man.

"Stand aside and let me see," my beloved ghost would say. "Why, isn't what you're embracing my pink cactus, that has survived me? How amazingly it's grown and changed! But now that I look into your face, my child, I recognise it. I recognise it by your agitation, by your air of waiting, by the devotion in your outspread hands, by the beating of your heart and your suppressed cry, by the growing daylight all about you, yes, I recognise, I lay claim to all of that. Stay where you are, don't hide, and may you both be left in peace, you and the man you're embracing, for I see that he is in truth my pink cactus, that has at last consented to flower."

Is this house going to be my last? I weigh it up and listen to it during that short private night that enwraps us, here in the Midi, immediately after the hour of noon. The cicadas creak and so does the new wattle fencing that shelters the terrace, a nameless insect is crushing tiny grits between its shards, the reddish bird in the pine tree calls every ten seconds, and the west wind, circling watchfully round my walls, leaves unruffled the flat, dense, hard sea, whose harsh blue will soften towards nightfall.

Is this house going to be my last, the one that will find me faithful, the one I shall never leave again? It is so ordinary that it could have no rivals.

I hear the clink of the bottles being carried to the well from which they will be pulled up, cooled, for dinner to-night. One of them, red-currant pink, will accompany the green melon; the other, a sand-grown wine, amber-coloured and over-generous, goes with the salad of tomatoes, pimentos and onions soaked in oil, and with the ripe fruit. After dinner I mustn't forget to irrigate the little runnels that surround the melons, and to water by hand the balsams, phlox and dahlias, and the young tangerine trees, which haven't yet got roots long enough to drink unaided in the depths of the earth, nor strength to break into leaf without help, under the steady scorching of the heavens. The young tangerine trees, planted . . . for whom? I don't know. Perhaps for me. The cats will spring sideways at the moths when by ten the air is blue as a morning glory. The pair of Japanese hens, perching drowsily on the arm of a rustic armchair, will chirp like birds in a nest. The dogs, already far away from this world, will be thinking of the coming dawn, and I shall have the choice of a book, bed, or the coast road studded with fluting toads.

To-morrow I shall surprise the red dawn on the tamarisks wet with salty dew, and on the mock bamboos where a pearl hangs at the tip of each blue lance. The coast road that leads up from the night, the mist and the sea; then a bath, work and rest. How simple everything could be! Can it be that I have attained here what one never starts a second time? Everything is much as it was in the first years of my life, and little by little I recognise the road back. The way my country house has grown smaller, the cats, the aged bitch, my sense of wonder and a serenity whose breath I can feel from far off—a merciful moisture, a promise of healing rain hanging over my still-stormy life—all these help me to recognise it. Many stretches of the road have been completed and left behind. A castle inhabited for a moment has melted into the distance, replaced by this little house. Properties scattered over France have dwindled little by little in response to a wish that in times past I never dared to put into words. How wonderfully confident and vital must that past have been to inspire even the lowly guardian angels of the present: the servitors who have once again become humble and competent. The housemaid adores digging and the cook soaps the linen in the wash-house. Does there then exist here on earth a kitchen-garden path where I can retrace my own footsteps, a path I thought I should never follow again except on the other side of life? Is that maternal ghost, in the old-fashioned dress of blue sateen, filling the watering-cans on the edge of the well? This coolness of spray, this sweet enticement, this provincial spirit, in short this innocence, isn't all this the charm of declining years? How simple everthing has become! Everything, even to the second place that I sometimes lay opposite my own on the shady table.

A second place doesn't take much room now: a green plate, a thick antique glass, slightly cloudy. If I say that it is to be taken away for good, no pernicious blast will blow suddenly from the horizon to make my hair stand on end and alter the direction of my life, as once it did. If that place is removed from my table I shall still eat with appetite. There is no longer any mystery, no longer a serpent coiled under the napkin ringed, to distinguish it from mine, with a brass lyre which once held in place, at the top of a music-stand of the last century, the loose pages of a score where only the down-beats were marked, spaced at intervals as regular as tears. This place belongs to the friend who comes and goes, and no longer to a master of the house given to treading the resounding boards of a bedroom up above during the night. On days when the plate, the glass and the lyre are not in front of me, I am merely alone, and not abandoned. Now that my friends are reassured about that, they trust me.

Very few, only two or three, remain of those friends who in former days thought they saw me going under in my first shipwreck: for I honestly thought so myself and said as much to them. To these, one by one, death is bringing rest. I have friends who are younger, and in particular younger than I. I instinctively like to acquire and store up what looks like outlasting me. I have not caused such great torments to these, at most a few cares: "There now, *He's* going to spoil her for us again. . . . How long is *He* going to remain so important?" They would speculate on the outcome of the disease, its crises and its temperature chart: "A dangerous typhoid or a mild rash? Confound the woman, why does she always manage to catch such serious complaints!" My true friends have always given me that supreme proof of devotion, a spontaneous aversion for the man I loved. "And what if this one disappears too, what a lot of trouble it will give us, what a job to help her recover her balance!"

But at bottom they never grumbled greatly—very much the other way—when they saw me coming back to them overheated by the struggle, licking my wounds, counting my tactical errors, revelling in being biased, heaping crimes on the enemy who defies me, then whitewashing him out of all measure, then secretly hugging his letters and pictures: "He was charming. . . I ought to have . . . I ought not to have . . ." Then reason would return, bringing with it the calm that I do not like and my belatedly courteous, belatedly reserved silence which is, I really believe, the worst moment of all. Such is the routine of suffering, like the habitual clumsiness of those in love, and the compulsion which makes every couple innocently poison their home life.

Then is that militant life, that I thought I should

never see the last of, over and done with? I have nothing left now but my dreams with which to revive from time to time a dead love, by which I mean love purged of its brief and localised pleasures. Sometimes it happens that in a dream one of my loves begins again with an indescribable noise, a tumult of words, of looks that can be interpreted in two or three contradictory ways, of demands. Without any break or transition, the same dream ends in an exam in decimal fractions for the lower certificate. And if when I wake the pillow under the nape of my neck is a bit damp, it is because of the lower certificate. "A second longer and I should have failed in the oral", stammers memory, still caught in the toils. "Ah, that look he had in my dream! Who? The highest common factor? No, of course not, He, He when he used to spy on me through the window, to see if I had deceived him. But it wasn't He, it was . . . was it?" The light mounts, forcibly enlarging the gilded green field of vision between my eyelids. "Was it He, or else . . . ? I'm sure it's at least seven o'clock—if it's seven it's too late to water the aubergines—the sun is on them. And why, before I woke, didn't I brandish under his nose that letter in which he promised me peace, friendship, a better mutual knowledge of ourselves and . . . it's the first time I've got up so late this whole season." For to dream, and then to return to reality, only means that our scruples suffer a change of place and significance.

A little wing of light is beating between the two shutters, touching with irregular pulsations the wall or the long heavy table where we write or read or play, that eternal table that has come back from Brittany, as I have come back. Sometimes the wing of light is pink on the pink-washed wall, and sometimes blue on the blue cotton Moroccan rug. Dressers stacked with books, armchairs and chests of drawers have made a roundabout journey with me over fifteen years, through two or three French provinces. Elegant armchairs with tapering arms, countrified like peasant girls with delicate limbs, yellow plates that sing like bells when you rub them with your finger, dishes of thick white glaze—we are all astonished to find ourselves back in a country that is our own. For is not the house of my father and my grandparents on the Mourillon, fifty miles from here? It is true that other regions have cradled me, and some of them roughly. A woman lays claim to as many native lands as she has had happy loves. She is born, too, under every sky where she has recovered from the pain of loving. By that reckoning this blue salt shore, bright with tomatoes and pimentos, is doubly mine. How rich it is, and what a lot of time I've spent not knowing of it! The air is light, the grapes ripen so quickly that they are dried and wrinkled on the vine by the sun, the garlic is highly flavoured. That noble bareness that thirst sometimes confers on the soil, the refined idleness that one learns from a frugal people—for me these are late-discovered riches. But let me not complain. My maturity is the right time for them. My angular youth would have bled at the touch of the striated, mica-spangled rocks, the forked pine-needles, the agave, the spines of the sea-urchin, the bitter, sticky cistus and the fig tree, the underside of whose every leaf is a wild beast's tongue. What a country! The invader endows it with villas and garages, with motor-cars and dance-halls built to look like *Mas*. The barbarians from the north parcel out the land, speculate and deforest, and that is certainly a great pity. But during the course of the centuries how many ravishers have not fallen in love with such a captive? They arrive plotting to ruin her, stop suddenly and listen to her breathing in her sleep, and then, turning silent and respectful, they softly shut the gate in the fence. Submissive to your wishes, Provence, they fasten on your vine-leaf crown again, replant the pine tree and the fig, sow the variegated melon and have no other desire, Beauty, than to serve you and enjoy it.

The others will inevitably abandon you. Once upon a time they would have dishonoured you. But one horde more or less doesn't matter to you. Those who have come on the strength of a casino, an hotel or a post-card will leave you. They will flee, burnt and bitten by your wind white with dust. Keep your lovers, who drink water from the pitcher and the dry wine that ripens in the sand; keep those who pour oil religiously and turn away their heads when they pass in front of dead animals; keep those who rise early and lull themselves asleep in bed in the evening to the faint chugging of the pleasure-boats in the bay. Keep me. . . .

The ripening colour of the half-light marks the end

of my siesta. The prostrate cat will now for a certainty stretch herself to a phenomenal length, produce from her body a front paw whose exact length no one knows, and say, with a yawn like a flower: "It's long past four o'clock." The first motor-car is not far off, rolling on its little cloud of dust towards the shore; others will follow it. One of them will stop for a moment at the gate, and out of it there will pour on to the path, amid the feathery shade of the mimosas, men-friends without their wives and women-friends with their lovers. I haven't yet got to the point of shutting my gate in their faces and baring my teeth behind it. But the tone of my cordiality, familiar but cold, does not deceive them, and keeps them in check. The men like my dwelling, without a master; they like its smell, its doors with no locks. Some of the women say, with an air of sudden ecstasy: "Oh, what a paradise!" and secretly tot up all it lacks. But both the women and the men appreciate the patience with which I, who have no projects of my own, listen to theirs. They are "mad about this country", they want "a very simple little farm", or to build "a *mas* on this headland above the sea, by Jove, what a view!" At that point I become charming because I listen and say: "Yes, yes." For I do not covet the field alongside, I am not buying my neighbour's vineyard, and I'm not "adding a wing". There's always one of my comrades who eyes my vines, walks from the house to the sea without going up or down a step, returns and concludes: "The long and the short of it is that this property, just as it is, suits you perfectly."

And I say "Yes, yes", as I do when he or someone else assures me: "You don't change!", which means: "We've made up our minds that you never will change any more."

I'd very much like to try once again.

The door leading to the vines from the enclosure walled with openwork bricks is straining slightly on its hinges; the wind must be rising. It will swiftly sweep a quarter of the horizon and fasten on the wintry purity of the greenish north. Thereupon the whole hollow of the bay will boom like a shell. Goodbye to my night in the open on the raffia mattress! If I had persisted in sleeping out of doors, that powerful mouth that breathes coldness and drought, deadens all scents and anaesthetises the earth, the enemy of work, voluptuousness and sleep, would have torn off me the sheets and blankets that it knows how to twist into long rolls. What a strange tormentor, as intent on man as any wild beast! Those who are highly strung know more about it than I do. My Provençal cook, when the wind strikes her near the well, puts down her buckets, holds her head and cries: "It's killing me!" On nights when the mistral blows she groans under it in her little hut among the vines, and perhaps she sees it.

Having retired to my bedroom I wait with controlled impatience for the departure of this visitor for whom no sanctum is private, and who is already pushing under my door a strange tribute of withered petals, finely sifted seeds, sand and battered butterflies. Be off with you, I've discouraged other tokens before now; and I'm no longer forty, to avert my eyes at sight of a fading rose. Is that militant life over and done with then? There are three good times for thinking of it: the siesta, a short hour after dinner when the rustling of the newspaper, just arrived from Paris, seems oddly to fill the room, and then the irregular insomnia of the small hours, before dawn. Yes, it will soon be three o'clock. But even during these precarious small hours, that merge so quickly into day, where can I find that great cavern of bitterness promised me by my past griefs and joys, as well as my own books and those of others? Humble as I always am when I'm faced with anything I don't understand, I'm afraid of being mistaken when I imagine that this is the beginning of a long rest between myself and men. Come, Man, my friend, let us simply exist side by side! I have always liked your company. Just now you're looking at me so gently. What you see emerging from a confused heap of feminine cast-offs, still weighed down like a drowned woman by seaweed (for even if my head is saved, I cannot be sure that my struggling body will be), is your sister, your comrade: a woman who is escaping from the age when she is a woman. She has, like you, rather a thick neck, bodily strength that becomes less graceful as it weakens, and that authority which shows you that you can no longer make her despair, or only dispassionately. Let us remain together; you no longer have any reasons now for saying goodbye to me for ever.

Love, one of the great commonplaces of existence, is slowly leaving mine. The maternal instinct is another great commonplace. Once we've left these behind, we find that all the rest is gay and varied, and that there is plenty of it. But one doesn't leave all that behind when or as one pleases. How wise one of my husbands was when he remonstrated: "But is it impossible for

"There is about a very beautiful child something I can't define which makes me sad. How can I make myself clear? Your little niece C. is at this moment ravishingly beautiful. Full face she's still nothing much, but when she turns her profile in a certain way and you see the proud outline of her pure little nose below her lovely lashes, I am seized with an admiration that somehow disturbs me. They say that great lovers feel like that before the object of their passion. Can it be then that, in my way, I am a great lover? That's a discovery that would much have astonished my two husbands!"

So she was able, was she, to bend over a human flower with no harm to herself, no harm save for that "sadness"; was sadness her word for that melancholy ecstasy, that sense of exaltation which uplifts us when we see the waxen purity of faces dissolving into an arabesque never resembling its original, never twice the same: the dual fires of the eyes, the nostrils like twin calyxes, the little sea-cave of the mouth quivering as it waits for its prey? When she bent over a glorious childish creature she would tremble and sigh, seized with an anguish she could not explain, whose name is temptation. For it would never have occurred to her that from a youthful face there could emanate a perturbation, a mist like that which floats above grapes in their vat, nor that one could succumb to it. My first communings with myself taught me the lesson, though I failed to observe it sometimes: "Never touch a butterfly's wing with your finger."

"I certainly won't . . . or only just lightly . . . just at the tawny-black place where you see that violet glow, that moon-lick, without being able to say exactly where it starts or where it dies away."

"No, don't touch it. The whole thing will vanish if you merely brush it."

"But only just lightly! Perhaps this will be the time when I shall feel under this particular finger, my fourth, the most sensitive, the cold blue flame and the way it vanishes into the skin of the wing—the feathers of the wing—the dew of the wing . . ." A trace of lifeless ash on the tip of my finger, the wing dishonoured, the tiny creature weakened.

There is no doubt that my mother, who only learned, as she said, "by getting burnt", knew that one possesses through abstaining, and only through abstaining. For a "great lover" of her sort—of our sort—there is not much difference between the sin of abstention and that of consummation. Serene and gay in the presence of her husband, she became disturbed, and distracted with an unexplained passion when she came in contact with someone who was passing through a sublime experience. Confined to her village by her two successive husbands and four children, she had the power of conjuring up everywhere unexpected crises, burgeonings, metamorphoses and dramatic miracles, which she herself provoked and whose value she savoured to the full. She who nursed animals, cared for children and looked after plants, was spared the discovery that some creatures want to die, that certain children long to be defiled, that one of the buds is determined to be forced open and then

you to write a book that isn't about love, adultery,
semi-incestuous relations and a final separation?
Aren't there other things in life?" If he had not been
in such a hurry to get to his amorous rendezvous—for
he was handsome and charming—he might perhaps
have taught me what can take the place of love, in a
novel or out of it. But he went and I continued
obstinately covering that same bluish paper, gleaming
at this moment from the dark table to guide my hand,
with chapters dedicated to love or regret for love,
chapters blind with love. In them I called myself Renée
Néré or else, prophetically, I introduced a Léa. So it
came about that both legally and familiarly, as well as
in my books, I now have only one name, which is my
own. Did it take only thirty years of my life to reach that
point, or rather to get back to it? I shall end by thinking that it wasn't too high a price to pay. Can it be that
chance has made me one of those women so immersed in
one man that, whether they are barren or not, they carry
with them to the grave the shrivelled innocence of an old
maid? At the thought of such a fate my plump double
that I see in the sloping mirror, tanned by sun and sea,
would tremble, if it could still tremble at a past danger.

A hawk-moth from the oleanders is banging against
the fine wire-netting in front of the French window,
returning to the charge again and again until the taut
netting reverberates like the skin of a drum. It is cool.
The generous dew trickles, the mistral has put off its
offensive. The stars, magnified by the damp and salty
air, twinkle broadly. Once again the most beautiful of
all nights precedes the most beautiful of all days, and
not being asleep, I can enjoy it. Let us hope to-morrow

will find me equally sweet-tempered! In all sincerity I no longer ask for anything except what I can't have. Has someone broken my spirit, that I should be so gentle? Not at all: it's a very long time since I knew anyone really wicked—knew them face to face, bosom to bosom and limb to limb. As for an authentic villain, the real thing, the absolute, the artist, one rarely meets him even once in a lifetime. The ordinary bad hat is always in part a decent fellow. It's true that the third hour of the morning encourages indulgence in those who enjoy it in the open and have an assignation with no one but themselves beneath the deepening blue of their window. The crystalline emptiness of the sky, the already conscious sleep of the animals, the chilly contraction that closes the calyxes up again, are so many antidotes to passion and iniquity. But I don't need to be feeling indulgent in order to say that in my past no one has broken my spirit. I was made to suffer, oh yes, certainly I learnt how to suffer. But is suffering so very serious? I have come to doubt it. It may be quite childish, a sort of undignified pastime—I'm referring to the kind of suffering a man inflicts on a woman or a woman on a man. It's extremely painful. I agree that it's hardly bearable. But I very much fear that this sort of pain deserves no consideration at all. It's no more worthy of respect than old age or illness, for both of which I'm acquiring a great repulsion: both of them are anxious to get me in their clutches before long, and I'm holding my nose in advance. The love-sick, the betrayed and the jealous all smell alike.

I remember very definitely that when I was wretched because I had been disappointed in love, my animals loved me less. They scented my grief, that great admission of failure. I have seen an unforgettable look in the eyes of a beautiful well-bred bitch, a look still generous but restrained and politely bored, because she no longer loved as much all that I stood for—a man's look, the look of a certain man. Shall we never have done with that cliché, so stupid that it could only be human, about the sympathy of animals for man when he is unhappy? Animals love happiness almost as much as we do. A fit of crying disturbs them, they'll sometimes imitate sobbing, and for a moment they'll reflect our sadness. But they flee unhappiness as they flee fever, and I believe that in the long run they are capable of boycotting it.

What a good use the two tom-cats fighting outside are making of the July night! Those unearthly songs of the male cat have accompanied so many nocturnal hours in my life that they have become a symbol of wakefulness, of ritual insomnia. Yes, I know it is three o'clock and that I'm going to fall asleep again, and that when I wake I shall be sorry to have missed the moment when the milky blueness begins to rise up from the sea, reaches the sky and flows over it until it stops at a red rift flush with the horizon.

The great voice of a baritone wild beast, long drawn out, persists through the sharp sounds of a tenor cat, clever at tremolos and at shrill chromatic scales interrupted by furious innuendoes growing more nasal the more insulting they become. The two tom-cats do not hate each other, but the clear nights suggest battle and declamatory dialogues. Why sleep? They make their choice and in summer take only the best parts of the night and the day. They choose. All animals who are

well treated choose whatever is best in us and in their
surroundings. It was the realisation of that that helped
me to emerge from the period when their comparative
coldness revealed to me my own lack of dignity. I
choose the phrase, lack of dignity, advisedly. Surely
I ought to have thrown off that sordid domination? It
was all in such deplorable taste, those half-dried tears,
that melodrama. What opinion of a woman like that
could one expect from an animal, a bitch for instance,
herself compact of hidden fire and secrets, a bitch who
had never groaned under the whip or wept in public?
She despised me, that goes without saying. And though
I didn't hide my hurt from the eyes of my fellows, I
blushed for it in her presence. It is true that she and I
loved the same man. But for all that it was in her eyes that
I read a thought that I've read in one of my mother's last
letters: "Love is not a sentiment worthy of respect."

One of my husbands used to suggest to me: "When
you're about fifty you ought to write a sort of hand-
book to teach women how to live in peace with the
man they love, a code for life as a couple." Perhaps I
am writing it now. O Man, my former loves, how one
gains and learns in your company! Yet the best of
friends must part; but I pledge myself here to take my
leave courteously. No, you have not broken me, perhaps
you never meant me any harm. Farewell, dear Man,
and welcome to you too. Across my bed which, since
I am in good health, is better arranged for writing than
a sick bed, a blue light creeps until it reaches the blue
paper, my hand and my bronze-coloured arm; the smell
of the sea warns me that the hour when air is colder
than water is at hand. Shall I get up? To sleep is sweet.

leaves, scraping off greenfly and questioning seeds
sleeping in the earth, how I wish I could have put
before it my own mirror of long ago: that tender face,
so little virile, that gave me back my own image
beautified! I would have said to my mother: "Look.
See what I'm doing. Measure what it's worth. Is it
worth my assuming a tarnished reputation in order to
nourish in secret, mouth to mouth, the prey that
people think I am myself absorbing? Is it worth my
turning away from those dawns that you and I love,
to give myself to eyelids that I dazzle and their promises of stardom? Judge, better than I can, my hesitant
work that I've gazed at too much. Trim your hard
gardener's nail!" But it was too late. By the time I
confessed all that to her she had already attained her
everleasting morning twilight. She would, alas, have
judged us plainly, with that divine cruelty of hers
which was innocent of wrath. "Pluck off that rather
unnatural shoot of yours, my daughter, that graft that
doesn't want to thrive except on you. It's a mistletoe.
I assure you it's a mistletoe. I'm not saying to you that
it's a bad thing to take on a mistletoe, because evil
and good can be equally resplendent and fruitful.
But . . ."

When I try to invent what she would have said to
me, there is always one place at which I falter. I lack
the words, above all the essential argument, the unexpected and equally enchanting blame and indulgence
which fell from her so lightly, slow to touch and gently
penetrate my clay, and then come to the surface again.
Now they well up in what I write and sometimes they
are thought beautiful. But I know well that, though

recognisable, they are deformed by my personal notions, my limited unselfishness, my half-hearted generosity and my sensuality whose eyes, thank God, were always bigger than its belly.

Each of us had two husbands, but whereas both of mine—I'm glad to say—are very much alive, my mother was twice a widow. Since she was faithful out of tenderness, duty and pride, my first divorce upset her greatly and my second marriage still more. Her odd explanation of this was: "It's not so much the divorce I mind, it's the marriage. It seems to me that anything would be better than marriage—only it isn't done." I laughed and pointed out that on two occasions she had set me an example. "I had to," she answered. "After all I belong to my village. But what are you going to do with so many husbands? It's a habit that grows and soon you won't be able to do without it."

"But Mother, what would you do in my place?"

"Something stupid, no doubt. The proof is that I married your father."

If she was afraid to say how great a place he had held in her heart, her letters, after he had left her for ever, told me of it, as did also an outburst of tears on the day after my father was buried. That day she and I were tidying the drawers of the yellow thuya-wood desk from which she took letters, the service records of Jules-Joseph Colette, Captain of the First Regiment of Zouaves, and six hundred gold francs—all that remained of a landed fortune, the fortune of Sidonie Landoy, frittered away. My mother, who had shown

no signs of weakness as she moved about surrounded
by relics, came across this handful of gold, gave a cry,
melted into tears and said: "Oh, dear Colette! He'd
told me, eight days ago, when he could still speak to
me, that he was only leaving me four hundred francs!"
She sobbed with gratitude, and I began that day to
doubt whether I had ever truly loved. No, certainly, a
woman as great as that could not commit the same
"stupidities" as I, and she was the first to discourage
me from imitating her:

"So this Monsieur X means a lot to you, does he?"

"But Mother, I love him!"

"Yes, yes, you love him. . . . All right then, you
love him."

She thought again, refrained with an effort from
saying what her celestial cruelty dictated, then burst
out once more:

"No, no, I'm not happy."

I pretended to be modest, dropped my eyes to
shut in the image of a handsome, envied, intelligent
man, with a glowing future, and replied gently:

"You're difficult."

"No, I'm not happy. I preferred, yes really I preferred the other one, the boy you now consider less
than the dust."

"Oh Mother! He's an idiot!"

"Yes, yes, an idiot. . . . Exactly."

I still remember how she bent her head, half-closing
her grey eyes to dwell on the dazzling, flattering picture
of the "idiot". And she added: "What beautiful things
you'd write with the idiot, Minet-Chéri! With the
other, you'll spend your time giving him all your most

precious gifts. And what if on top of that he makes
you unhappy? It's more that likely."

I laughed heartily: "Cassandra!"

"All right then, Cassandra. And if I were to say all I
foresee . . ." The grey eyes, half-closed, read the
future: "Fortunately you're not in too much danger."

At the time I did not understand her. No doubt she
would have explained herself later on. I know now
what she meant when she said "you're not in danger",
an ambiguous phrase referring not only to the calami-
ties I risked. To her mind I had already got over what
she called "the worst thing in a woman's life: her first
man". He is the only one you die of. After that,
married life—or a semblance of it—becomes a career,
and sometimes a system of bureaucratic rule in which
the only thing that distracts us and takes us out of
ourselves is that balancing trick which, at the ap-
pointed time, impels the greybeard towards the flapper,
and Chéri towards Léa.

Then, in obedience to the law of the climacteric, we
can at last triumph over what I will call the ordinary
run of lovers, provided we don't let this become a
sordid habit. But it is essential that this triumph should
be born of a cataclysm, die in the same way, and not
allowed to feed a contemptible regular hunger. Any
love, no matter what, if one lets it have its way, tends
to turn itself into a sort of alimentary canal, seizing
every opportunity of losing its exceptional quality, its
tormentor's nobility.

"Autumn is the only vintage time"—perhaps that is
true in love too. It is the season for sensual affection,
a time of truce in the monotonous succession of

struggles between equals, the perfect time for resting on a summit where two slopes meet. Autumn is the only vintage time; and a mouth still stained with a purplish drop, like a dried tear, of a juice that was not yet the true wine, has the right to proclaim it. Oh the eager joy of vintage, the haste to cast into the wine-press on the same day both the ripe grape and the verjuice, the rhythm which leaves far behind the ample, dreamy cadence of harvest, the pleasure, redder than other pleasures, the songs and drunken shouts! Then silence, withdrawal, the sleep of the new wine sealed up, removed from those stained hands that did it violence! It pleases me to think that hearts and bodies suffer a similar fate: I have paid for my folly, shut away the heady young wine that intoxicated me, and folded up my big, floating heart, emptied of its three or four marvels. How well it has fought and striven! There, there, heart, gently now, let us take a rest. You despised happiness, we can do ourselves that justice. Cassandra, to whom I'm returning and who did not dare foretell everything, did tell us this: that we were in no danger of dying for love nor, God be praised, of thinking ourselves content with a modest little happiness.

Now that I'm far away from that period of my life when I inclined only in one direction, like those allegorical figures at the source of rivers, cradled and drawn along by their watery tresses, I can let it diminish. It is true that I gave myself without stinting, or at least I thought so. If one poses as a classical Goddess of Plenty, whose job is to empty her cornucopia no matter where, one risks the critical stare of the public circling round the pedestal and appraising the statue according to its weight of over-handsome womanhood: "Hmm ... Doesn't one get a bit thinner when one gives out so much? How's this one managed to put on so much flesh?" People like you to waste away as a result of giving and they are quite right. The pelican is not expected to grow fat, the only way the ageing mistress can prove her selflessness is by letting a noble consumption make her pale, thereby leaving the field to a youthful cheek whipped with pink, and a ruddy lip. This rarely happens. On the contrary, to be perverse enough to gratify an adolescent lover up to the hilt doesn't ravage a woman sufficiently. Giving becomes a sort of neurosis, a fierce egotistical frenzy. "Here's a new tie, a cup of hot milk, a shred of my own live flesh, a box of cigarettes, a conversation, a journey, a kiss, a word of advice, the shelter of my arms, an idea. Take! And don't dream of refusing unless you want me to burst. I can't give you less, so put up with it!"

When a mother is still young and a mistress mature, rivalry in giving can poison both feminine hearts and cause a snarling hatred, a war of vixens in which it isn't the mother's clamour that is the less savage and the less indiscreet. Poor over-loved sons! Preening under feminine glances, wantonly nuzzled by the female who carried you, favourites from the deep night of the womb, beautiful cherished young males, whatever you do you can't help betraying when you pass from one mother to another. You yourself, my very dear mother, whom I liked to think untouched by my ordinary crimes, even in your correspondence I find, conveyed in a handwriting that strove in vain to hide the irregular pounding of your heart, these words: *"Yes, like you I've found Madame X very changed and sad. I know there is no mystery in her private life; so we can bet that big son of hers has his first mistress."*

If all one had to do, in the hope of one day running dry, were to keep on giving of oneself in great gushes, we "over-forties" could hardly fail. I know some who would accept the challenge right away: "Agreed! First that hell, which I can't do without; just one demon and afterwards peace, emptiness, blessed total peace, penury. . . ." How many sincerely hope that old age may arrive like a vulture that detaches itself from the sky and drops, after soaring for long invisible? And what then is old age? I shall learn. But when it comes I shall no longer be able to understand it. You, my very dear elder, will have disappeared without teaching me what old age is, for you wrote to me: *"Don't worry so much about my alleged arteriosclerosis. I'm better, and the proof is that at seven o'clock this morning I did the washing in my stream. I was enraptured. What a pleasure it is to dabble in clear water! I sawed wood, too, and made six little bundles of firewood. And I'm doing my housework myself again, which means it's being properly done. And after all, I'm only seventy-six!"*

You wrote to me that same day, a year before you died, and the loops of your capital B's, T's and J's, which have a kind of proud cap on the back of their

heads, are radiant with gaiety. How rich you were
that morning in your little house! At the end of the
garden leapt a little stream, so swift that it immediately carried away everything that might have sullied
it. You were rich with yet another morning, with a
new victory over illness, rich with one more task, with
the jewels of light glittering in the running water,
with one more truce between you and all your pains.
You were soaping linen in the stream, sighing because
you could not get over the death of your beloved, you
went "twee-e-e-e!" at the chaffinches, you were
thinking that you would tell me about your morning,
oh, you hoarder of treasure! What I amass is not of the
same quality, but whatever of it may endure comes
from the parallel though inferior seam, mixed with
clay. And I haven't taken too long to understand that
an age comes for a woman when, instead of clinging
to beautiful feet that are impatient to roam the world,
expressing herself in soothing words, boring tears and
burning, ever-shorter sighs—an age comes when the
only thing that is left for her is to enrich her own self.

She hoards and reckons up everything, even to
blows and scars—a scar being a mark which she did
not carry at birth, an acquisition. When she sighs,
"Oh, what a lot of sorrows He endowed me with!"
she is, in spite of herself, weighing the value of the
word—the value of the gifts. Little by little she stows
them tranquilly away. But there are so many of them
that in time she is forced, as her treasure increases, to
stand back a little from it, like a painter from his work.
She stands back, and returns, and stands back again,
pushing some scandalous detail into place, bringing

into the light of day a memory drowned in shadow. By some unhoped-for art she becomes—equitable. Is anyone imagining as he reads me, that I'm portraying myself? Have patience: this is merely my model.

When a man's glance is following certain household preparations, especially those for a meal, there is apt to be a look on his face that combines religious attention, boredom and fear. Like cats, men dread sweeping, and the lighted stove, and soapy water being pushed with a broom over the tiled floor.

In honour of a local saint, who according to tradition presides over merry-makings, Segonzac, Carco, Régis Gignoux and Thérèse Dorny were to leave their hillside and eat a southern luncheon here: salads, stuffed *rascasse* and aubergine fritters, an everyday meal which I usually enriched with a roast bird.

Vial, who lives in a thimble painted pink three hundred metres away, was not happy that morning because the portable stove we used for ironing, fitted up as a charcoal grill, was taking up a corner of the terrace. So he made himself as small as a sporting dog on a wedding day.

"Vial, don't you think they'll like my sauce with the little chickens? Four little chickens split in half, beaten with the flat of the chopper, salted, peppered, and anointed with pure oil brushed on with a sprig of *pebreda*? The little leaves of the *pebreda*, and the taste of it, cling to the grilled flesh. Look at them, don't they look good!"

Vial looked at them and so did I. Good indeed! A little rosy blood remained in the broken joints of the plucked and mutilated chickens, and you could see the

shape of the wings, and the young scales coverir
the little legs that had only this morning enjoye
running and scratching. Why not cook a child, too!
My tirade petered out and Vial said not a word. I
sighed as I beat my sharp, unctuous sauce, but soon
the aroma of the delicate flesh, dripping on to the
charcoal, would give me a yawning hunger. I think I
may soon give up eating the flesh of animals; but not
to-day.

"Tie my apron for me, Vial. Thank you. Next
year . . ."

"What are you going to do, next year?"

"I shall be a vegetarian. Dip the tip of your finger
in my sauce. Well? That sauce on tender little
chickens . . . All the same—not this year, I'm too
hungry—all the same I shall be a vegetarian."

"Why?"

"It would take too long to explain. When one stops
liking a certain kind of cannibalism, all the other kinds
leave of their own accord, like fleas from a dead
hedgehog. Pour me out some oil, gently. . . ."

He bent his bare body, polished by sun and salt.
His skin caught the light, so that he was green round
the loins and blue on the shoulders, according as he
moved, like the dyers of Fez. When I said "Stop!" he
cut short the thread of golden oil and straightened
himself, and I laid my hand caressingly for a moment
on his chest, as one does with a horse. He looked at
my hand, which proclaims my age—in fact it looks
several years older—but I did not withdraw it. It is a
good little hand, burnt dark brown, and the skin is
getting rather loose round the joints and on the back.

It has nails cut short, a thumb that readily bends back like a scorpion's tail, scars and scratches, and I'm not ashamed of it, rather the reverse. It has two pretty nails—a present from my mother—and three not very beautiful—a souvenir of my father.

"You've bathed? You went for a good four hundred metres along the shore? Well then why, when we're only in July, do you look as though it were the end of the holidays, Vial?"

The slightest emotional upset disturbs Vial's regular, rather beautiful features. He hasn't a gay expression, but he never looks sad. I say he's handsome because here, after a month's stay, all the men are handsome as a result of the hot sun, the sea, and their going naked.

"What have you brought me from the market, Vial? You didn't mind, did you? Divine only just had time to run and get the chickens."

"Two melons, an almond tart, and peaches. There are no more early figs and the others won't be ripe till . . ."

"I know that better than you, I inspect them every day in my vineyard. You're a darling. How much do I owe you?"

He shrugged to show he didn't know, his beautifully muscled shoulders rising and falling like a bosom breathing.

"You've forgotten? Wait while I see how big the melons are. That tart is the sixteen-franc size, and you have two kilos of peaches. Fourteen and sixteen make thirty, thirty and fifteen, forty-five. I owe you between forty-five and fifty francs."

"Have you got on your bathing-suit under your apron? Haven't you had time for a bathe?"

"Of course I have."

He licked the top of my arm, quite simply.

"It's true."

"Oh, you know, that might be yesterday evening's salt. Let's rest a bit, we've lots of time, they'll all be late."

"All right. Isn't there something useful I can do?"

"Yes, get married."

"Oh! I'm thirty-five."

"That's what I mean. It'll make you younger. You aren't young enough. That comes with age, according to Labiche. Your little friend didn't come back from the market with you? You must have met her on the port?"

"Mademoiselle Clément is finishing a study at Le Lavandou."

"You don't like my calling her your little friend, I see?"

"No, I don't. It's an expression that might make people think she's my mistress, when she's not."

I laughed as I powdered the overhot embers in the ironing-stove. I hardly know the type to which this boy, who lives very quietly, belongs. He is of the same generation as Carco, Segonzac, Léopold Marchand and Pierre Benoit, Mac-Orlan, Cocteau and Dignimont—those whom I knew when they were, as I like to say, "quite little", before and during the war. Was it at that time, when the irregular ebb and flow of leave used to bring them to Paris, that I got into

the habit of *tutoying* nearly all of them on the strength
of their faces, some oddly fat and others as hollow as
those of schoolboys grown too fast? No, it's simply
because they are young, and if they greet me with
hugs and big smacking kisses on the cheek, that's also
because they are young. But if the most sensitive
among them—those that I've named and those
I don't name—call me "Madame" and, for fun, "my
good master", that is because they are they and I
am I.

The almost naked youth who poured the oil for me
this morning took part in the war too. When it was
over, just as he was going to become an upholsterer
again, he jibbed. He was afraid, he said, of a father
who had remained vigorous, grasping in his business,
and arrogant. I've sometimes wanted to write a story
about a family devoured, bones and all, by its parents.
I'd use as my model, for instance, Mme Lhermier,
who kept her daughter tied to her apron-strings, prevented every chance of marriage and turned the stupid
docile girl into a sort of withered twin of herself, who
never left her day or night, and never complained.
But one day I saw the look on Mlle Lhermier's face. . . .
Horror! Horror! I should borrow a few characteristics
from Albert X, a passionate victim and disturbing
shadow of his mother; and from Fernand Z, a frail
banker who waits in vain for the death of his robust
banker father. There are plenty of them, I should only
have to choose. The trouble is that Mauriac has already
done *Genitrix*. But I mustn't waste too much pity on
Vial the son, whose Christian name is . . . What at
this early stage!

"Vial, what's your Christian name?"

"Hector."

In my astonishment, I stopped trimming the stalks of the first dahlias of the season that I had cut for the table.

"Hector? I had an idea you were called . . . Valère."

"So I am, but I wanted to make sure you'd more or less forgotten it."

. . . on Vial the son, who artfully makes the most of his long commercial apprenticeship and uses visiting-cards inscribed "*Vial, Decorator*". He is no longer an upholsterer. He has a modest little shop in Paris, half fancy-bookshop, half knick-knacks, the kind you see everywhere. And because he likes the company of painters he has taken to liking their paintings.

Among all the scribblers who have no time for anything but writing, he gives himself the luxury of reading, designing furniture and even criticising us. He tells Carco that he ought never to have published anything but verse, and Segonzac that he is a mystic. The great "Dédé" doesn't laugh, and answers politely: "Scoundrrrel! Son of a bitch, there's something in that, your head's better scrrrewed on than your backside!" Carco calls me to witness: "If a professional writer said that to me, Colette, I'd call him a fat-head. But what on earth can I say to an upholsterer? Mr Interior-decorator, you come it too strong!"

I don't know much more about my oil-pourer. But what do I know of my other friends? What we're doing, first and foremost, when we seek friendship or

give it is to cry: "Sanctuary! Sanctuary!" That cry is
certainly the best thing in us, so we may as well keep
the rest dark as long as possible.

I think that the presence of human beings in any
number tires plants. Horticultural exhibits swoon and
die almost every evening, when people have paid
them too much attention; I found my garden weary
after the departure of my friends. Perhaps flowers are
sensitive to the sound of voices. And my flowers are
no more accustomed to receptions than I am.

My guests gone, the cats creep out of their lairs,
yawn, stretch as they do when they come out of their
travelling baskets, and sniff the traces of the intruders.
The sleepy tom-cat glides down from the mulberry
tree like a liana. His ravishing companion, on the
terrace which is given over to her again, displays her
belly where there appears, in a cloud of bluish fur, a
single rosy teat, for this season she has suckled only
one kitten. The departure of the visitors in no way
changes the habits of the Brabançon bitch who watches
over me, doesn't stop and never has stopped watching
over me, and will only at death cease to give me her
whole attention. Her death alone can put an end to the
drama of her life: to live with me or without me. She
too is ageing sturdily.

Grouped round these three specimens of the ruling
caste of animals, the second-rate creatures keep the
place assigned them by a protocol not so much human
as animal: the scrawny she-cats from the neighbouring
farms, my caretaker's dogs transformed by a bath of

white dust. "In summer here all the dogs belong to the eighteenth century," says Vial.

The swallows were already drinking in the wash-house and snapping up the mayflies when my "company" took itself off. The air had its stale afternoon flavour and it was very hot in the sun, which sets late. But it cannot deceive me, I decline with the day. And towards the end of each day the cat, winding herself about my ankles in a figure of eight, invites me to celebrate the approach of night. She is the third cat in my life, if I count only the cats of real character, memorable among both cats and she-cats.

Shall I ever marvel enough at animals? This one is exceptional, like a friend one will never replace, or a perfect lover. What is the source of the love she bears me? Of her own accord she adapted her pace to mine, and the invisible bond that links her to me gave me the idea of a collar and a leash. She got both and she wore them as though she were sighing: "At last!" Her narrow little lean face, rain-blue with eyes of pure gold, looks older and seems to get paler when the slightest thing worries her. She has the modesty that belongs to perfect lovers, and their dread of too-insistent contacts. I shall not say much more about her. All the rest is silence, faithfulness, impacts of soul, the shadow of an azure shape on the blue paper that receives everything I write, the silent passage of paws silvered with moisture.

After her, but a long way after, I have the tom-cat, her magnificent husband, all slumbrous with beauty and power, and as timid as a professional strong man. Then come all the creatures that fly, crawl and creak, the hedgehog of the vines, the innumerable lizards that the grass-snakes eat, the nocturnal toad which, when I gather it into the palm of my hand and hold it up towards the lantern, lets two crystal cries fall into the grass. The crab under the seaweed too, and the blue gurnard with martlet's wings that rises in flight from the waves. If it falls on the sand I pick it up stunned, encrusted with grit, and then put it back in the water and swim beside it, supporting its head. But I no longer like describing the appearance or writing stories of animals. The passage of the centuries never bridges the chasm which yawns between them and man. I shall end by hiding my own creatures except from a few friends, whom they shall choose. I shall show the cats to Philippe Berthelot, himself full of feline power, and to Vial, who is in love with the she-cat and pretends, as does Alfred Savoir, that I can conjure up a cat in a place where no cat exists. One doesn't love beasts and men at the same time. I am becoming daily more suspect to my fellows. But if they were my fellows I should not be suspect to them.

"When I enter a room where you're alone with your animals," my second husband used to say, "I feel I'm being indiscreet. One of these days you'll retire to a jungle." I keep toying with the agreeable picture of the future this prophecy offers me, though I've no wish to try and fathom what insidious—or impatient—suggestion may have lain behind it; but I dwell on it to remind myself of the deep, logical mistrust which it reveals in a very civilised man. I dwell on it as on a sentence written by the finger of a man on a forehead which, if one pushes aside the foliage of hair that covers it, probably smells, to a human sense of smell, of a lair, the blood of a hare, the belly of a squirrel, a bitch's milk. Any man who remains on the side of men has reason to shrink from a creature who opts for beasts and who smiles, strong in her dreadful innocence. "Your monstrous simplicity. . . . Your sweetness full of dark places. . . ." How true all those phrases were! From the human point of view monstrosity begins where there arises connivance with animals. Did not Marcel Schwob dub "sadistic monsters" those withered old bird-charmers one used to see in the Tuileries covered with birds? Connivance alone would be one thing but there is preference too, and at this point I shall keep silent. I stop short also when it comes to arenas and menageries. For if I see no objection to putting into the hands of the public, in print, rearranged fragments of my emotional life, it's understandable that I should tie up tight in the same sack, strictly private, all that concerns a *preference* for animals and—it's a question of partiality too—the child whom I brought into the world. How charming she is, that child, when she scratches, in a thoughtful, friendly way, the granular head of a huge toad. . . . Ssh! Once upon a time I took upon myself to make a girl of fourteen or fifteen the heroine of a novel. May I be forgiven, for I did not then know what I was doing.

"You'll retire to a jungle. . . ." So be it. And I mustn't wait too long. I mustn't wait until I notice the first waverings in the graph of my relation and exchanges with animals. The wish to captivate, in other words to dominate, the different ways of wrapping up a wish or an order and directing them to their end, these I feel are still flexible in me—but for how long?

A poor lioness, a beautiful creature, recently picked me out from the bunch of gapers massed before her bars. Having chosen me she came out of her long despair as out of a sleep, and not knowing how to show that she had recognised me, that she wanted to confront me, to question me, perhaps to love me to the point where she could accept only me as a victim, she threatened, sparked and roared like a captive fire, hurled herself against the bars and then suddenly, wearied, grew drowsy, still looking at me.

The mental hearing, that I can project towards the Beast, still functions. The tragedies of birds in the air, the subterranean combats of rodents, the suddenly increased sound of a swarm on the warpath, the hopeless look of horses and donkeys are so many messages addressed to me. I no longer want to marry anyone, but I still dream that I am marrying a very big cat. No doubt Montherlant would be delighted to learn it.

Love and respect for living creatures could be read in my mother's letters and in her heart. So I know where the spring of my vocation lay, a spring which I muddied as soon as I was born through my passion for touching and stirring up the depths lying beneath the pure stream. I accuse myself of having from an early age, not content with loving them, wanted to shine in the eyes of these, my kin and my accomplices. It is an ambition I still have.

"So you don't like fame?" Madame de Noailles asked me.

But I do. I would like to leave a great reputation among those creatures who having kept, on their fur and in their souls, the trace of my passage, madly hoped for a single moment that I belonged to them.

My team of young guests was very attractive this morning. Two had brought with them young women who were extremely pretty, and so well behaved that you might think each of them had been told: "I'm going to take you to Colette's, you know, but I must remind you that she doesn't like bird-like cries or literary views. Put on your prettiest frock, the pink one, or the blue. You'll pour out the coffee." They know that the young women I find agreeable are pretty and rather reserved. They are well aware of the things that charm my leisure hours: children, ceremonious young women, and saucy animals.

Some painters have wives or mistresses who are worthy of them and of the life they lead. They look gentle and have the same sort of habits as farmers' wives. For don't the men get up at daybreak and go off to the fields or the forest or along the shore? And don't they return at nightfall, tired and silent with solitude? While they are away the women cut out summer frocks from tablecloths, or make napkins and serviettes out of cotton handkerchiefs, and go to market without affectation, that is to say to buy provisions and not to exclaim at the "beautiful consistency" of the red-lacquered *rascasses* or the bellies of the *girelles*, striped oche and azure.

"My man? He must be in the fields, over there

towards Pampelonne", answers the mistress of Luc-
Albert Moreau, pointing to the horizon with the vague
gesture of a peasant woman. Asselin sings like a cow-
herd and sometimes, if you strain your ear, the breeze
brings you the sweet voice of Dignimont, chanting a
little soldier's or sailor's lament.

Hélène Clément, who came alone, was by no means
the plainest. She doesn't belong in the camp of the
models, nor in that of the women who are submissive
to men. She is a straw blonde, with straight hair. The
sun tans her a harmonious red, a beautiful even red
that floods her blonde skin and pledges her grey
eyes to remain blue all summer. Tall, and slenderly
built, almost her only fault is that she is too straightforward physically and morally, which is one of the
snobberies that you find in girls of twenty-five. It is
fair to say that I don't know her very well.

She paints in an obstinate way, with big virile
strokes, swims, drives her five-horse-power car, and
often goes to see her parents, who spend the summer
in the mountains because they dread the heat. She lives
in a *pension de famille* so that everyone knows that she
is a "serious-minded girl". Thirty years ago one met
Hélène Clément at seaside places, a piece of embroidery in her hand. Nowadays she paints the sea and
rubs herself with coconut oil. She has the same pretty,
docile countenance as the Hélène Cléments of other
days, the same bodily dignity and above all the
deferential way of answering: "Yes, Madame. Thank
you, Madame" which, cropping up in the middle of
the language she has learnt from the painters and the
wild young men, half opens the garden gate of the

boarding school again. What I like in this big creature
is precisely that air of having let fall her old embroidery, that embroidery which in her took the place of
mystery. I may be mistaken, because I do not pay
enough attention to Hélène. Perhaps too the trans-
parency of body and soul which she seems to prize
so much lets me guess too easily the presence of that
sad irresolution which—though they deny it—is
characteristic of those so-called independent women
who do no wrong—if one is still, as in former days, to
call carnal intercourse "wrong".

No one else will come. I shan't leave this table for the
little café at the port where people gather to watch the
flamboyant sunsets. Towards the end of the day
the sun gathers together the scraps of cloud evaporated
by the warm sea, draws them to the sky's rim and
twists them into rags of fire, then stretches them out
into ruddy bands and, as it touches *Les Maures*,
burns itself out. But this month it sets too late. I shall
admire it well enough as I dine alone, my back against
the wall of my terrace. I've had my fill of pleasant
faces to-day. So instead the bitch, the she-cat and I will
walk towards that great spread of violet that rises
from the sea and shows where the East lies. Soon it
will be the hour when some old people return home,
neighbours of mine who work in the fields. I can only
bear old people when they are bent earthwards,
chapped and chalky, with hands like wood and hair
like a bird's nest. Some of them offer me, in the
hollow of a palm drained of human moisture and
colour, the most precious thing they have managed to
procure: an egg, a chicken, a round apple, a rose, a

grape. A Provençal woman of seventy-two goes every day from the port to her field of vines and vegetables, two kilometres in the morning and the same in the evening. No doubt she will die of toil, but she doesn't seem tired when she sits down for a moment before my gate. She gives light cries: "My! How pretty it is!" I hurry there: with a carved, blackened, hooked finger she is stroking the flat-headed bud, like a snake ready to hiss, of one of those sea-shore lilies that shoot out of the earth, grow so quickly that one dare not look at them, spread forth their corollas and their maleficent odour like that of a ripe, bruised fruit, and then return to nothingness.

No, it was not pretty. It looked like a strong, blind young serpent. But the old woman knew that it would be pretty a few days later. She had had time to learn that. There were moments when, seeing her laden with green peppers, a necklace of new onions round her neck, her hands of dried osier half-closed on an egg she never lets fall, I could love her if I didn't suddenly recollect that, though she no longer has the strength to create, she keeps the strength to destroy, and that she crushes the shrew-mouse on the path, the dragon-fly against the window-pane, and the still-moist newborn kitten. She makes no distinction between that and shelling peas. So that is why, when I pass her, I say "Goodbye!" and let her fade into the landscape, her and her shadow, a tiny old man who lives like a lizard in a stone hut under an oleander. The old woman talks, the old man no longer does. He has nothing left to say to anyone. No longer able to dig, he scratches the earth, and when he sweeps the threshold of his hut he looks as if he were playing because he uses a child's broom. The other day they found an old person dead and quite dry, like a dead toad burnt up by the mid-day heat before a bird of prey had had time to gut it. Death becomes more decent to our living eyes when it is thus cheated of much of its corruption. Will my own final lot be that of a light friable body, hollow bones and a great devouring sun over it all? Sometimes I force myself to think of it so as to persuade myself that the second half of my life is making me take a little more thought and care for what happens *after*. . . . The illusion soon passes. Death does not interest me— not even my own.

We have dined well. We have walked on the coast road, along its most populated part, the narrow flowery marsh where hemp agrimony, statice and scabious contribute three shades of mauve, the tall flowering reed its cluster of brown edible seeds, the myrtle its white scent—white, white and bitter, pricking the tonsils, white to the point of causing nausea and ecstasy—the tamarisk its rosy mist and the bulrush its beaver-furred club. This place teems with life, especially at daybreak and when the birds are going to bed. The reed warbler slides endlessly, for fun, down the stems of the reeds and each time shouts for joy. The swallows skim the sea, the tits, drunk with courage, expel from this paradise the troops of jays, thirsty wasps and poaching cats; and in the middle of the day, heavy Camberwell Beauties, trailing the thick velvet of their wings, yellow *Flambés*, striped like tigers, and swallow-tails with gothic veining flutter over the sickly-sweet little lagoon, salted by the sea and sweetened by roots and grasses, and come to pump the honey from the pink agrimony, the bird's-foot trefoil and the mints, each butterfly voluptuously attached to its flower.

In the evening animal life hides a little but barely diminishes. What secret laughter there is, what swift leapings under my footsteps, what lightning flights before the spring of the two cats who have followed me! For in their night livery they are redoubtable. The gentle she-cat shoots through the bushes with a single bound while her powerful male, once aroused, scatters the stones of the road like a horse as he gallops along, and both of them, without hunger, crunch the glowing-eyed hawkmoths.

The cool of the evening here brings for me a shiver that resembles a laugh, a cloak of fresh air on my bare flesh, and a feeling of pity which tightens its grip on me as night closes in. If I had any confidence in that moment of gentleness, then would be the time for me to grow in stature, to adopt a brave attitude, to dare and die. But every time I avoid it. To grow. . . . For whom? To dare. . . . What more could I dare, then? I've been told often enough that to live first as love dictates, and then as the absence of love dictates, shows the most overweening conceit. It's so good to be flush with the earth, to become once more a prey to plants just tall enough to provide shade for my fore-head, paws which reach up to seek my hand, furrows asking for water, a tender letter that wants an answer, a red lamp in the green of the night, a notebook of

smooth paper that I must embroider with my writing
—I am back again, as I am every evening. How near
the dawn is! This month night gives herself to the
earth as to a secret lover, quickly and a little at a time.
It is ten o'clock. In four hours it will no longer be real
night. Besides, a great round mouth of a moon, rather
frightening, is invading the sky, and she is no friend
of mine.

Three hundred metres away Vial's lamp, in his
thimble-shaped house, looks at mine. Whatever can
the boy be up to, instead of shuffling in his *espadrilles*
along to the little port, or dancing—he dances so well
—at the little dance-hall on the jetty? He's too quiet.
One of these days I must give my mind to the question
seriously, and marry him to that other sober creature,
Hélène Clément—oh, only for as long as they want. I
noticed to-day a shade of difference in her, in her
expression that's to say, when she spoke to him. She
was laughing with all the others, especially when
Carco, his eyelids half-closed like a hunter's over his
caramel-coloured eyes, revealed to her the shocking
and prodigious secret of an old prostitute who managed to retain her childish innocence for twenty-five
years in the Latin Quarter. Hélène isn't prudish about
what she hears, far from it. But her laugh, at Carco's
stories, is for all that the laugh of that long-ago
Hélène Clément who dropped her embroidery frame
when her cousin the polytechnician—"Oh, Henry, will
you be quiet!"—told her, as he pushed the swing, that
he had caught a glimpse of her ankle. Hélène Clément
reserves for Vial that side of her that is closest to
truth: the serious face of a girl who only wants to be

simple. It isn't possible that Vial should not have noticed it.

Normally I am not much given to making plans for two people to be happy together, but I have the feeling that I am responsible for that uncomfortable little agitation, that setting in motion of idle forces which might in future engulf two beings hitherto far apart, each safely sheltered in personal privacy, or lack of it.

When I was driving my little car to market yesterday morning, about nine o'clock, I passed and then picked up Hélène Clément who, her bare head glossy as a golden apple, was on her way, with a canvas under her arm, to the carpenter who acts as frame-maker. Two hundred metres further on, behind his gate and on the threshold of the "Thimble", Vial was scraping an antique armchair, as dry, convoluted and delicate as a hawthorn in winter.

"Vial, we haven't seen you for two days! What's that armchair, Vial?"

His laugh was a white bar in his dark face.

"You're not going to have this one! I went further than Moustier-Sainte-Marie to get it, with the Citroën."

"So that was it," said Hélène.

Vial raised his head, his smile fading.

"What d'you mean, that was it?"

She said nothing and gave him so dangerously stupid a look that he could have read what he liked in those grey eyes, wide open in the sun. I jumped out of the car.

"Show us, Vial, do show us! And treat us to a

morning glass of white wine and cold water!"

Hélène got out after me and sniffed the smell of the
unfamiliar little dwelling, furnished with a divan and
a half-moon-shaped ship's table and brightened with
pink linen hangings and white Moustier pottery.

"A Juan Gris, two Dignimonts, a colour print by
Linder," counted Hélène. "That's Vial all over, always
chopping and changing. You think that's the right
thing for the walls of a house down here?"

Vial, who was wiping his stained hands, looked at
Hélène. She was leaning with one hand against the
wall, neck and arms braced as if for a climb, and her
bare feet in sandals as she stood on tiptoe were far
from ugly. And how beautiful that red earthenware
colour of her whole body, so lightly clad!

"Vial, how much did you pay for your armchair?"

"A hundred and ninety francs. And it's walnut,
under the paint that some brute has covered it with.
Look at the arm I've scraped. . . ."

"Vial, sell it to me!"

He shook his head.

"Vial, are you a dealer or aren't you? Vial, have you
no heart?"

He shook his head.

"Vial, I'll swop your armchair for . . . for Hélène,
there now!"

"Is she yours then?"

For wit and delicacy there was nothing to choose
between my jest and his reply.

"That's settled then!" bantered Hélène. "Really, my
dear, you've got a bargain!"

She laughed, redder than her red sunburn, and in

each of her grey blue eyes danced a glittering speck of light. But Vial once again shook his head and the two glittering specks changed to tears.

"Hélène!"

Already she was running away from the house and Vial and I looked after her.

"What's the matter with her?"

"I don't know," said Vial coldly.

"It's your fault."

"I didn't say anything."

"You went 'no, no' like this."

"And if I'd gone 'yes, yes' like this, would it have been better?"

"You bore me, Vial, I'm going. I'll tell you to-morrow how it turns out."

"Oh, you know . . ."

He shrugged a shoulder, let it fall, and walked with me to the garden gate.

In my little car a dry-eyed Hélène was humming as she gazed at the freshly-painted picture balanced on her knees.

"D'you see anything in this, Madame Colette?"

I found a few words to say as I looked at the straightforward study, which she had unnecessarily overpainted in order to be "a real painter", and then, forgetting prudence, I added, "Did Vial hurt you? I do hope not."

She answered me with a coldness that seemed to me exactly like Vial's. "I beg of you, Madame Colette, don't confuse humiliation with pain. Yes, yes, humiliation. Accidents like that often happen to me in this particular milieu."

"What milieu?"

Hélène made a slight movement of the shoulders, compressed her lips, and I felt she was displeased with herself. Then she turned to me with a sudden burst of honesty which made my little car skid on that poetic road that is never repaired.

"Madame Colette, don't take what I say amiss. I say 'this milieu' because after all it isn't the milieu in which I was brought up. I say 'this milieu' because although I like it very much I sometimes feel an outsider among the painters and their girl-friends. But all the same I'm intelligent enough to . . ."

". . . to understand life."

She protested with her whole body.

"I beg you, Madame Colette, don't treat me—you sometimes do!—like a little bourgeoise who's playing at being a 'Montparno' type. I do indeed understand quite a few things, and above all that Vial, who doesn't belong to 'this milieu' either, doesn't go down well when he jokes in a certain way and permits himself certain liberties. He puts neither grace nor gaiety into it, and what would be charming and jolly on the lips of either Dédé or Kiss, for instance, sounds shocking on his."

"But he didn't say anything," I put in as I pulled up in front of the "First Class Pension" where Hélène stays.

Standing by the little car and holding out her hand, my young passenger could not conceal her irritation, or the glitter in her eyes, moist once again, in which was reflected the triumphant blue all about us.

"If you don't mind, Madame Colette, let's say no

more about it. I have no wish to let this story, which
isn't one, drag on for ever, even for the pleasure of
listening to the defence of Vial, above all presented by
you! ... Presented by you!"

She fled, rather too big for such childish misery. I
called after her: "Goodbye! Goodbye!" in a kind way,
so that our brusque separation should not awaken the
curiosity of the sculptor, Lejeune, who at that moment
was crossing the little square. He was dressed, in all
innocence, in *eau de Nil* cotton shorts with a sleeveless
pink jacket, open over a sweater embroidered with
little flowers in cross-stitch, and he greeted us by
raising a wide-brimmed rush hat trimmed with woollen
cherries.

It was because of that silly Hélène that I bore with
Vial's presence absentmindedly on the following
afternoon, and enjoyed it less than usual. Yet he had
brought me some bars of nougat, and branches of a
carob tree with green fruit, which keep fresh a long
time if one sticks them in earthenware jars full of moist
sand.

After the five o'clock bathe he was sprawling
indolently on the terrace, as he did every day. It had
been a wind-whipped bathe, and so cold under a
fierce sun—for the Mediterranean is full of surprises
—that instead of the shelter of the pink room we
sought the warm, living, beaten earth under the
checkered shade of wide-spaced branches. Five
o'clock in the afternoon is a wavering golden hour
which momentarily ruffles the universal blue of air and

water in which we bathe. The wind had not yet risen but a ripple was noticeable among the featheriest foliage, that of the mimosa, for instance, and a faint signal waved by one branch of a pine was answered by another pine branch, which nodded all by itself.

"Vial, don't you think it's less blue than yesterday?"

"What is less blue?" murmured Vial, bronze in his white slip.

He was lying nearly flat, his forehead on his folded arms; I always like him better when he hides his face. Not that he is ugly, but the lines of his face look rather sleepy above his clear-cut, alert, expressive body. I haven't omitted to point out to Vial that he might be guillotined without anyone's noticing.

"Everything is less blue. Or else it may be me. Blueness is mental. Blue doesn't make you hungry, or voluptuous. A blue room is uninhabitable. . . ."

"Since when?"

"Since I've said so! Unless you no longer hope for anything—in which case you can live in a blue room."

"Why me?"

"By you I mean anybody."

"Thank you. Why have you got blood on your leg?"

"It's my own. I stumbled against that commonest of shore plants, the broken bottle "

"Why is your left ankle always a little swollen?"

"And what about you, why were you caddish to the little Clément girl, come to that?"

The bronze man sat up, with an air of dignity.

"I wasn't caddish to the . . . to Mademoiselle Clément. But if what you have in mind is a marriage, I shall be infinitely obliged to you, Madame, if you'll stop talking to me about her!"

"How romantic you are, Vial! Mayn't we have a little laugh? Move along, you're taking up all the room on this parapet, and let me tell you, you don't know everything. When she left me yesterday she forbade me to undertake your defence. And she swept off like a tragedy queen repeating 'Above all not you! Above all not you!' Would you believe it?"

Vial leapt to his feet and planted himself before me, black as a baker's boy from hell.

"She said that to you? She dared?"

He faced me with a look so wide-eyed, so comically unlike himself, that I couldn't keep a straight face—I laugh more easily than I used to. The look of respectability which Vial's frequent silences, his habit of looking down and a certain sureness in his attitude give him, disintegrated completely and I did not find him pretty. He pulled himself together with a pleasing promptness and sighed casually, "Poor little thing!"

"You're sorry for her?"

"What about you?"

"Vial, I don't much like your habit of always answering a question by another question. It's not polite. As far as I'm concerned, you realise, I can hardly be said to know the girl. . . "

"Neither do I."

"Oh! I thought . . . But she isn't difficult to know. She gives the impression of shunning mystery as

though it were a microbe. Hullo! Coo-ee! Isn't that
Géraldy, coming back from Les Salins?"

"Yes, I think it is."

"Why didn't he stop?"

"He didn't hear you, the noise of his gears drown
all other sounds."

"But he did, he looked round. It's you who frightened him. I was saying to you that little Hélène
Clément . . ."

"Will you excuse me? I want to go and get my
sweater. People from the north call Provence a hot
country. . . ."

Vial took himself off and I became more aware of
the warmth, the freshness, the increased slant of the
light, the universal blue, a few sails on the sea, and the
near-by fig tree spreading its odour of milk and
flowering grass. A tiny little tuft of fire was smoking
on a mountain. The sky turned pink where it touched
the harsh azure of a Mediterranean, as ripply as an
animal's coat, and the she-cat for no apparent reason
began to smile at me. The thing is that she loves
solitude, by which I mean my presence, and her smile
made me realise that for the first time I was treating
Vial as a third party of importance.

His absence left me with a sense of emptiness and
airy well-being; did that mean that his presence was
enough to fill up the former and prevent the latter?
At the same moment I understood that the reason why
Géraldy had not interrupted the noise of his tortured
engine in front of my door was because Vial, visible
from the road, was with me; and that if my friends
and companions had all quietly given up coming

round about five o'clock to my crescent-shaped bay where the sand, under the weight of blue water, is so firm and white, it was because they felt sure that they would meet there, in addition to myself, the half-silent, vaguely-bored Valère Vial, keeping his distance, running with the hare but hunting with the hounds.

That's all it is, a slight misunderstanding. I've thought it well over, not for long, since there's no point in thinking for long at a time and there's nothing in this particular matter that merits it. I can't believe that this young man is in any way calculating. It is true that, though I've often been taken in, I've not learnt to be suspicious. What I would rather fear, for him, is some form of amorous attachment. I write that without laughing, and, raising my head, I look at myself, without laughing, in the inclined mirror; then I turn to my writing again.

No other fear, not even that of ridicule, prevents me from writing these lines which I am willing to risk will be published. Why should I stop my hand from gliding over this paper to which for so many years I've con-fided what I know about myself, what I've tried to hide, what I've invented and what I've guessed? At no time has the catastrophe of love, in all its phases and consequences, formed a part of the true intimate life of a woman. Why do men—writers or so-called writers—still show surprise that a woman should so easily reveal to the public love-secrets and amorous lies and half-truths? By divulging these, she manages to hide other important and obscure secrets which she herself does not understand very well. The spotlight, the shameless eye which she obligingly operates, always explores the same sector of a woman's life, that sector tortured by bliss and discord round which the shades are thickest. But it is not in the illuminated zone that the darkest plots are woven. Man, my friend, you willingly make fun of women's writings because they can't help being autobiographical. On whom then were you relying to paint women for you, din them into your ears, debase them in your eyes, in short make you tired of them? On yourself? You have become my friend too recently for me to give you my opinion on that. We were saying, then, that Vial . . .

How beautiful the night is, once again! How good it is, in the depths of such a night, to contemplate seriously something that is no longer serious! Seriously, for it is no laughing matter. This is not the first time that a veiled, unfamiliar ardour has tried first to restrict and then to break the circle within which I live so trustingly. These involuntary conquests have nothing to do with a time of life. We must look for their origin in literature—and this is where my responsibility begins. I write this humbly and conscientiously. When readers take to writing to an author, especially to a woman author, they don't easily lose the habit. Vial, who has only known me for two or three summers, must still be trying to find me in two or three of my novels—if I dare call them novels. There are still young girls—too young to notice the dates of editions—who write to tell me they have read the *Claudine* books in secret and that they will look for my answer at the *poste restante* . . . if indeed they do not give me an assignation in a tea-shop. Perhaps they see me in a school-girl's uniform—who knows, in socks? Not long before his death Catulle Mendès said to me: "You won't be able to gauge until much later the power of the literary type you've created." Why did I not ignore all masculine suggestions and create a type which by its simplicity and even by its resemblance would have been more worthy to endure? But let us go back to Vial and Hélène Clément. . . .

A worn old moon is wandering along the horizon pursued by a surprisingly neat and metallic-looking little cloud, grabbing at the bitten disk as a fish grabs a floating slice of fruit. There is still no promise of rain there. We want rain for the gardens and the orchards. The unfathomable blue of the night, powdered with stars, makes my rather bare pink walls look pinker still when I turn and look at them. An oriental coolness clings to the walls, and the sparse pieces of furniture breathe at their ease. Only in this sun-steeped country can a heavy table, a wicker chair, an earthenware jar crowned with flowers, and a dish whose thick enamelling has run over the edge, make a complete furnishing. Segonzac decorates his "hall", vast as a barn, with rustic trophies only: crossed scythes and rakes, two-pronged forks of polished wood, wreaths of wheat-ears and red-handled whips, whose plaited tresses add a flourish to the wall. In the same way in Vial's "Thimble" . . .

Yes, let's get back to Vial. I am capering round Vial to-night in the way that a filly plays up before the start and then, after countless frolicsome curvettings, gently faces the tapes. I am not afraid of being emotionally stirred; but I am afraid of being bored. I am afraid of the appetite for drama and solemnity that young people have—especially Hélène Clément. How pleasant Vial was yesterday! Already he's less so. I compare his look to-day with that of yesterday. In spite of myself I see a meaning in his good-neighbourly faithfulness, in his long silences and in his favourite attitude, his head resting on his folded arms. I try to interpret his outbursts of questioning, evoking the sound of them: "Is it true that . . . who could have given you the idea of such a character? Didn't you know So-and-so, about the time when you were writing such-and-such a book? . . . I say, if I'm being indiscreet, send me packing. . . ." And then this evening, to crown all, when he repeated: "She dared! She dared!", with all the histrionics of a juvenile lead.

So here—at a time of life when I accept only the flower of any pleasure and the best of whatever is best, since I no longer demand anything—here is a fruit out of season, ripened by my easy familiarity: "Hi, young man, stand me a dozen Portuguese oysters, here without sitting down, Marseilles fashion. To-morrow we'll get up at six, Vial, and go and buy roses at the Halles, them's my orders!"—and also by my reputation, which is open to various interpretations.

And what if I were to be less gentle, to myself and others, from now until the end of this beautiful Provençal season starred with gleaming geraniums, white frocks, and half-opened water-melons showing their hearts glowing like planets! Yet nothing was threatening my happy summer of blue salt and crystal, my summer of open windows and swinging doors, my summer of necklaces of young garlic white as jasmine.

The amorous attachment of Vial and the no less amorous resentment of the little Clément girl—however little I like it I am placed between those two streams of emotion. I'm trying to understand them and quickly jotting down my comments. No matter if I incur ridicule—but it's true, there is the ridiculous side of it. It is hardly worth my remembering it, since in a moment I shall have forgotten it. It wasn't from you, my very dear mother—where are you watching, at this hour of your daily watch?—that I could have learnt this hesitation at the moment for helping, with hand and shoulder, an exhausted cart-horse, of gathering up a muddy dog in the fold of a skirt, of persuading and sheltering a shivering hostile child that was none of ours, or of shouldering impartially the weight of a stammering love in danger of falling into more mortal abysses. If I insert into our common liability some disorder that you don't recognise, forgive me. "*At my age there is only one virtue left: not to hurt anyone.*" It was you who said that. I haven't, my very dear, your light step for treading certain paths. I remember how, on rainy days, you hardly ever had mud on your shoes. And I still see your light foot making a detour to spare a little grass-snake, stretched out happily on a warm path. I haven't got the blind certainty with which you blissfully examined both "good" and "evil", nor your art of giving new names, according to your code, to embittered old virtues and poor sins that have been waiting for centuries for their share of paradise. What you shunned in virtue was its pestilential austerity. How I love that letter of yours: *"The tea was given in honour of some very ugly women. Were we celebrating their ugliness? They bring their sewing and they work and work with an application that gives me the creeps. Why does it always seem to me that they are doing something evil?"* Sickened, you sensed a kindliness that could easily have committed more than one crime.

Here is the dawn. To-day it is all little clouds like a shower of petals, a dawn for those with hearts at rest. Raising myself by my wrists I can perceive, already emerging from the shadow pursued by the light, a swallow-dark sea and the "Thimble", still with no real colour, the "Thimble" where lies a solitary young man, ripening one secret too many. Solitary . . . it's a beautiful-looking word, beginning with its capital S rearing like a protective serpent. I can't entirely isolate it from the fierce glitter it receives from the solitaire diamond, the fierce glitter of Vial. Poor fellow! Now why didn't I think of exclaiming "Poor Hélène Clément!"? I'm fond of catching myself red-handed. In Morocco I called on some owners of great farms, voluntary exiles from France, entirely devoted to their vast Moroccan lands. They had retained a strange practice, in reading the papers, of pouncing on the word "Paris" with the appetite and smiles of people at a feast. For me, O Man, you are the fatherland; is that why you remain the first of my cares? I see no reason why not. But now, you cares, you little summer love-affairs, you must die here as the shadow round my lamp is dying; the arrogant song of a blackbird comes rolling up to me like big round pearls dropping from a broken thread. The night-scented fragrance of the pines will soon dissolve in the rising sun. This is the perfect hour for going to search, in the half-awakened sea where each movement of my bare legs breaks an iridescent film of pink enamel on the heavy blue of the water, for that quilt of seaweed that I need to protect the foot of the young tangerine trees.

"Minet-Chéri,

It's not quite five in the morning. I'm writing to you by the light of my lamp and that of a fire just across the way, it's Mme Moreau's barn burning. Has someone set fire to it on purpose? It's full of fodder. The firemen are down there in my little garden. They're trampling on the borders I've prepared for flowers and strawberry plants. It's raining fire on my hen-house; what luck that I'd decided to rear no more chickens! It used to give me the horrors to eat, or make others eat, trusting hens that I had fed myself. How beautiful this fire is! I wonder if you've inherited my love of disasters? Oh dear, there go the poor rats that have escaped from the burning barn, squeaking and running in all directions. I expect they'll take refuge in my woodshed. Don't worry about anything else, by good fortune the wind is in the East. You realise that, if it were in the West, I should be roasted already. As I myself can be of no help, and since it's nothing but straw. I can give myself over to my love of tempests, the noise of the wind, and flames in the open air. . . . Now that I've reassured you by writing, I shall go and drink my morning coffee, and gaze at the beautiful fire."

"Naturally I don't dare offer you such a small thing," repeated Hélène Clément for the second time. The small thing, which she had brought me yesterday, was a seascape, seen between prickly pears zinc

blue against the chemical blue of the sea, a very concentrated study, as always a little too solid.

"Yet you came to offer it to me, Hélène?"

"Yes . . . because it's blue and because you like to
surround yourself with different blues. But one
shouldn't dare offer you such small things, should
one?"

Had she then seen "big things" in my house? With
a sweeping gesture I was able to clear myself of such
a charge. I thanked her and she graciously propped
her canvas up on the edge of a shelf, just where a
stiff little lightning-coloured sunbeam pierced the
shadow between two shutters. The canvas gleamed
with all its blues, showing up all its painter's tricks as
a made-up face reveals its secrets under the blaze of a
spot-light, and Hélène sighed.

"You see," she said, "it isn't good."

"What do you think is the matter with it?"

"That it's by me, that's all. By someone else it
would be better. Painting's difficult."

"So is writing."

"Do you mean that?"

She put this banal question to me in an anxious tone
of voice, full of incredulity and surprise.

"It certainly is."

In the half-light that I arrange and cherish, every
afternoon, with as much care as I would a bouquet,
the eyes of this young girl became dark green, and I
admired, below her hair that was no longer blonde,
the perfect, glowing, red earthenware of her neck, a
sturdy and supple column; long, like those of people
of limited intelligence, but at the same time thick,

revealing strength, the desire to succeed, and self-confidence.

"You were working, Madame?"

"No, never at this hour, at least not in summer."

"So I'm disturbing you less than if I'd come at another time."

"If you were disturbing me I should send you away."

"Yes. Would you like me to make you some lemonade?"

"No, thank you—unless you're thirsty? Forgive me, I'm being a very poor hostess."

"Oh!"

She made a vague gesture with her hand, picked up a book and opened it. The white page caught the gleam of bright light that clove the shadow and, like a mirror, reflected it upward on to the ceiling. For games of that kind the powerful summer light seizes the slightest object, brings it into the open and either glorifies it or dissolves it to nothing. The noon-day sun turns the red geraniums black and casts vertically down on us a sad, ashen light. At noon the only pure azure in the landscape is that of the short shadows huddled close at the foot of walls and trees. I was waiting patiently for Hélène Clément to go. She merely raised her arm to smooth her hair with the flat of her hand. Even without seeing her I should have known from this gesture that she was blonde, healthily and rather pungently blonde; blonde and upset, on edge—there was no doubt of it. Embarrassed, she quickly lowered her bare arm, a beautiful ruddy handle, still rather flat between the shoulder and the elbow.

"You have very pretty arms, Hélène."

She smiled for the first time since she had come in, and paid me the compliment of looking confused. For if women and young girls quite calmly receive compliments from men on particular attractions in their bodies, a word of praise from a woman flatters them more and makes them glow with a mixture of embarrassment and pleasure that sometimes goes quite deep. Hélène smiled and then shrugged her shoulders.

"Where does that get me, with my luck?"

"Could it get you somewhere then, if it weren't for your luck?"

I was artfully using in this case that method of the interrogative answer that I found fault with in Vial.

She looked at me frankly, helped by the half-light which changed her into a brown-haired young woman with dark green eyes.

"Madame Colette," she began without much effort, "you've been kind enough to treat me, last summer and this, as . . . really as a . . ."

"Little chum?" I suggested.

"Two days ago, Madame, chum is just the word I should have used. I should probably have added that I was sick of it, and sick of all the pals, or something equally personal. To-day I can't think of any slang. I hardly ever do think of slang with you, Madame Colette."

"I can get along without it, Hélène."

The child was heating my cool room and her emotion thickened the air. At first my only grudge against her was for that, and for shortening my day. And besides, I knew Hélène's secret and I was afraid of being bored. Already in thought I was escaping to the burning, beaten earth of the terrace and listening to the crickets, which, revived by my noticing them, were sawing the dog-day into tiny splinters. With a start I became aware of all that was shining on the other side of the shutters, and hesitated no longer to show my impatience with a "Well, Hélène?" that a grown-up woman would have taken for a barely polite dismissal. But Hélène is every inch a young girl and she showed it very clearly. She threw herself on that "Well?" with the simplicity of an animal that has never yet known a snare, and spoke.

"Well, Madame, I want to show you that I'm worthy of confidence . . . in short, of the welcome you've given me. I don't want you to think me either a liar or . . . In short, Madame Colette, it's true that I live in a very independent way and that I work. But after all, you know life well enough to understand that there are times when things aren't easy, that I'm a woman like any other . . . that one can't avoid certain affections . . . certain hopes, and it's just in that particular hope that I've been disappointed, cruelly disappointed, for I had reason to believe . . . In this very place, last year, Madame, he spoke to me in unambiguous terms."

Less out of malice than to allow her to draw breath, I asked: "Who?"

She pronounced his name musically: "Vial, Madame."

The reproach that I read in her eyes blamed, not my curiosity, but certainly the artifice which she judged unworthy of us. So I protested.

"I know very well it's Vial, my dear. And what can we do about it?"

She fell silent, half-opened her mouth and then bit her parched lips. While we were speaking the stiff shaft of sunlight, spangled with dust, had reached far enough to burn her shoulder and, as though it were a fly, Hélène moved her arm and brushed the spot of light away with her hand. What she still had to say did not pass her lips. She still had to say to me, "Madame, I believe you are the . . . the friend of Vial, and that is why Vial cannot love me." I might easily have said it for her, but the moments passed and neither of us made up our mind to speak. Hélène pushed her armchair back a little and the blaze of light caressed her face. I felt sure that in an instant the whole of that youthful planet, with its bare, rounded, moon-like forehead and cheeks, was going to crack up, rent by an earthquake of sobs. The white down round her mouth, as a rule scarcely visible, was beaded with a dew of emotion. Hélène wiped her temples with the end of her striped scarf. A passionate desire to be sincere, and the odour of an irritated blonde, emanated from her, although she kept silent with all her might. She implored me to understand, not to force her to speak; but I suddenly stopped troubling about her, in so far as she was Hélène Clément. I put her into her niche in the universe, among the spectacles of other days of which I had been the anonymous specta- tor or the proud begetter. That decent silly creature will never know that I held her worthy to rank in my memory with my tears for my adolescent joys: the shock of my first sight of a dawn of dark fire on an iron-blue peak covered with violet snow; the flower-like unfolding of the crinkled hand of a new-born babe; the echo of a single long note taking wing from the throat of a bird, low at first, then so high that I confused it, at the moment when it broke off, with the gliding of a shooting star; and those flames, my very dear, those dishevelled peonies of flame that the fire shook over your garden. You sat down happily, spoon in hand, *"since it was nothing but straw"*.

After that it's a relief to get back to Hélène, I must say. She was stammering, hampered by her uneasy love and her respectful suspicion. "So there you are!" I nearly said to her. A jilted girl doesn't have such an easy time of it. She talked of how ashamed she was, of how it was her duty to go "somewhere else", she blamed herself for having come to see me to-day and promised "never to come again, since . . ." She circled miserably round a conclusion hedged about by four or five terrible, barbed, impregnable words, "since you are the . . . the friend of Vial". For she wouldn't have dared say "the mistress".

She was soon far past that moment which had illumined the whole of her, and I watched my memories diminish, grow dim and darken.

"If you would at least say a word to me, Madame, only one word, even if it were only to throw me out. I have nothing against *you*, Madame, I swear it. . . ."

"But neither have I got anything against you, Hélène."

And then came the tears. Oh, these great galumphing girls, who don't hesitate to racket round on their own, drive their own cars, smoke coarse tobacco and abuse their father and mother!

"Come now, Hélène, come!"

As I write this, I once again experience a great feeling of repulsion for what took place this morning—it has not yet struck midnight. Only now do I dare to name the cause of my embarrassment, of my blushing and my clumsiness in articulating a few simple words: it is called timidity. When one leaves love and the practice of love behind, does that mean that one finds timidity again? Was it then so difficult to say what I finally did say to that weeping girl, begging for charity: "No, no, my child, you're imagining something extremely stupid. Nobody here is taking anything at all from anyone. I forgive you very willingly and if I can help you . . ."

This was more than the poor girl was asking for. She said "Thank you, thank you," and stammeringly extolled my "goodness" and wetted my hands with her kisses.

"Don't say '*vous*' to me, Madame, don't say '*vous*'. . . ." When I opened the door for her the setting sun enveloped the whole of her as she stood on my doorstep, with her crumpled white frock and her swollen eyes, laughing a little, moist, re-powdered, somehow touching. But I was suffering from my wretched timidity, face to face with that young Hélène in disarray. Disarray is not timidity. It is rather a kind of carelessness, a relish in letting oneself go.

My day has not been a pleasant one. I still have days and days before me, I suppose; but I no longer like spoiling them. Untimely timidity, slightly withered and bitter like anything which has been kept too long, equivocal and useless. It neither becomes me nor helps me.

A faint puff of sirocco wafts silently from one end of the bedroom to the other, ventilating the room no more than would a captive owl. When I have finished with these pages—the colour of daylight in the dark— I shall go and sleep on the raffia mattress out of doors. The whole sky wheels above the heads of those who sleep in the open, and if I wake once or twice before broad day, the course of the great stars, that I find no longer in the same place, makes me slightly giddy. Sometimes the end of the night is so cold that at three in the morning the dew traces a path of tears along the leaves, and the long hairs of my Angora blanket turn silver as a meadow. Ti-mi-di-ty, I have experienced timidity. Yet all I need have done was to speak of love and clear myself of suspicion. The thing is that fear of ridicule—even my own fear—restricts one. Can you imagine me proclaiming, with the blush of innocence on my forehead, that Vial . . .

Now I come to think of it, what about him in all this? The heroine is laying claim to all the limelight in this little story. She charges into the foreground, planting there her unambiguous colours and her unassailable respectability that is in such poor taste. And what of the man? He lies low and remains silent. What a relief!

The man in question did not remain silent for long. I was astonished to find how quickly Hélène's

thoughts, travelling subtly along three hundred metres
of coast and following the curves of the shore like a
thirsty bird, had broken into Vial's house and his
peace of mind. I didn't fail to notice that this morning,
instead of opening the gate and coming out surrounded
by the welcoming dogs, Vial leant against the gate and
called from a distance:

"It's the pair of us, Luc-Albert Moreau and me."

And with his arm he pointed out—strangely clad in
black with hands crossed, eyes as moist as those of a
doe and a look as patient and gentle as a country saint
—Luc-Albert Moreau.

"D'you need a sponsor, then?" I called to Vial.
"Come in, the pair of you!"

But Luc-Albert wanted to be off at once because he
was going to meet some new canvases and his wife,
the one bringing the others.

"You'll excuse me . . . not a canvas left in the
house . . . not a canvas left in the town. Acres and
acres of ruined canvases, all daubed by the Americans
and the Czechs. I paint on the bottoms of cardboard
hat-boxes. They say it's the station's fault. Oh, that
station! You know what that station's like. . . ."

As he spoke he seemed, with his hand curved like
a shell, to be absolving and blessing all that his word
condemned.

Under the ten o'clock sun the day was still young,
thanks to a brisk breeze coming in from the bay. A
gaiety in the light, the rustling of the mulberry trees,
the cool underside of the very great heat recalled the
month of June. The rejuvenated animals roamed about
as in spring, a great nocturnal hand seemed to have

wiped away two months from the earth. Deluded and cheered by this I finished without effort the mulching of the tangerine trees. In the circular trench two metres in diameter dug round their trunks I heaped seaweed freed from salt, then I covered it over with soil that I stamped down with my two feet as if I were treading grapes, and the spring wind dried my sweat as I went along.

To lift and penetrate and tear apart the soil is a labour—a pleasure—always accompanied by an exaltation that no unprofitable exercise can ever provide. The sight of upturned soil makes every living creature avid and watchful. The finches followed me, pouncing on the worms with a cry; the cats sniffed the traces of moisture darkening the crumbling clods; my bitch, intoxicated, was tunnelling a burrow for herself with all four paws. When you open up the earth, even for a mere cabbage-patch, you always feel like the first man, the master, the husband with no rivals. The earth you open up has no longer any past—only a future. With my back burnt, my nose gleaming and my heart pounding with a hollow sound like a footstep behind a wall, I was so absorbed that for a moment I forgot Vial. Gardening rivets eyes and mind on the earth, and when a shrubby tree has been helped, nourished, supported and cosily settled in its mulch covered with fresh earth, its expression, its happy look fill me with love.

"All the same, Vial, if it were really spring, how much more fragrant the earth would smell!"

"If it were really spring . . ." repeated Vial. "But in that case we should be far from here, and shouldn't be enjoying the fragrance of this earth."

"Just wait, Vial, soon I shall be coming here in the spring, and in the autumn, and also in those months that serve to fill in the gaps between two seasons—February, say, or else the second fortnight of November. The second fortnight of November, when the vines are bare. This tiny little tangerine tree, like a ball, don't you think it has a certain style already? Round as an apple! I shall try and keep it that shape. In ten years . . ."

Some invisible, unspeakable thing must be waiting for me at the end of that time, since I faltered over the ten years and could not go on.

"In ten years?" echoed Vial.

I raised my head to answer and thought that this well-built young man, fitting so neatly inside his beautiful brown skin, made, in spite of his white garment, rather a dark patch against the pink wall, the hollyhocks, the geraniums and dahlias of my enclosure.

"In ten years, Vial, one will pick beautiful tangerines from this little tree."

"You will pick them," said Vial.

"I or someone else, that doesn't matter."

"It does," said Vial.

He looked down his rather big nose and let me lift the full watering-can without helping me.

"Don't tire yourself, Vial!"

"Sorry. . . ."

He stretched out a bronze arm and a hand whose fingers were browned by the sun. There was an appreciable contrast between the strength of the arm, and the hand with its long fingers, and I shrugged my shoulders, disdaining the help of that hand.

"Pooh!"

"Yes, I know!"

Vial knows how to supply the missing words in a sentence and interpret an exclamation in the right way.

"I didn't . . . *think* that to hurt your feelings. When a man's hand is slender it's rather beautiful."

"It's rather beautiful, but you don't like it."

"Not for a labourer, naturally. Oh, I feel so congested I shall burst, quick, a bathe! The skin on my back's splitting, the upper part of my arms is peeling and as for my nose . . . Think of it, since half-past seven this morning! I look frightful, don't I?"

Vial looked at my face and hands; the sun made him blink as he turned his upper lip back over his teeth. His grimace changed into a woebegone little tremor and he answered "Yes."

It was, I admit, the one answer I wasn't expecting. And Vial's tone of voice made it impossible for me to make a joke of it. All the same I wanted to laugh as I wiped my neck and forehead. "Well, my boy, you don't exactly beat about the bush, do you?"

And I managed an awkward little feminine laugh, in order to insist "So you find me frightful and you tell me so?"

Vial was still staring at me, still with an expression of intolerant suffering, and he made me wait for his reply.

"Yes. For the past three hours you've been sticking at this idiotic—or, if you prefer, useless—work, just as you do everyday. For three hours you've been roasting in the sun, your hands are like the hands of a day-labourer, that old overall has lost its colour and you haven't condescended to powder your nose since this morning. Why, why do you do it? Yes, I know you enjoy it, that you're using up a kind of pugnacious fury. But there are other pleasures of the same kind—oh, I don't know, picking flowers, walking along the shore, putting on your big white hat and knotting a blue scarf round your neck. You have such beautiful eyes, when you want to. And what about giving a little thought to us who love you and who are worth just as much as those insignificant little trees, it seems to me . . ."

He felt his audacity petering out, and merely added, "It's true, all that!" out of pure sulkiness, shifting the soil with the tip of his foot.

The sun streamed down on his bronzed, well-shaven cheek. On such a face youth ought never to be dazzling. His chestnut-coloured eyes have depth and a flattering fringe of dark lashes. His mouth has the advantage of strong teeth and a groove dividing the upper lip. Vial will enjoy a decent old age, a time of maturity when people will say of him, looking at his long nose with its little hump, his firm chin and prominent eyebrows: "What a good-looking young man he must have been!" He will answer with a sigh: "Ah, if you'd known me at thirty! Without immodesty, I . . ." And it will not be true.

That was what I was thinking of as I wiped the nape of my neck and tidied my hair, in the presence of a man who had just addressed to me, for the first time

since we had known each other, words full of hidden
meaning. Yes indeed! What do people suppose we are
thinking when we look at men—and women—we
older women confined in a precarious, solitary sort of
security, face to face with the youth of other people?
It is true that we are pitiless in our judgments; and as
far as I am concerned, if I aspire to detachment, I
start from a solid basis. I say, "You're no longer any
use to me," before I get as far as saying "So I'd like
to be useful to you myself in some way." Am I going
to devote myself to someone again? Yes, if I can't
avoid it. To a man or to a woman, and as little as
possible. But I still feel myself too fragile for a perfect,
harmonious solitude, which reverberates with every
shock but keeps its shape, its open calyx turned
towards the living world.

All the same I was thinking of Vial as I looked at
Vial and rubbed the light, sandy, salty soil off my legs.
There was no need to reply at once, and perhaps I
enjoyed prolonging the silence wherein I moved at my
ease, *"since it was nothing but straw . . ."*, and since my
timidity, yesterday's ti-mi-di-ty, had vanished. O Man,
friend or foe, façade that faithfully reflects and sends
back to us everything that we throw at you, born
interlocuter! I stepped confidently over my latest
seed-bed.

"Come on then, Vial, my boy. We'll go and bathe
and afterwards I've something to say to you. If you'd
like to lunch with me, there are stuffed sardines."

It happened that the bathe, disturbed by the fear of
sharks, brought us neither silence nor intimacy. This
is the month when they stray into the bays, and up the

mouths of rivers; the other day my neighbour ran his boat aground against the flank of a shark; his boat lacked draught and he found himself in a ticklish situation. The tourists of the neighbourhood, and my summer companions, about ten in number, were revelling in the contrast between the fresh weather and the warm bathe. As for the shark, we're prudent enough to fear this annual menace. When we dive, we keep our eyes open in the jellyfish-coloured, clouded crystal water, and the least, unexpected, shadow of a cloud, sailing along the sea-bed of white sand, sends us quickly back to the surface, out of breath and none too proud of ourselves. Naked, wet, and defenceless, this morning we felt as united as a group shipwrecked in the Antipodes, and some mothers were calling back their paddling children as though to shelter them from a flight of assegais and the tentacles of an octopus.

"They say," said Géraldy, half his body out of the water like a mermaid, "that *bambinos* in the Pacific play with the sharks, swimming under water and kicking them on the nose. Like this . . ."

"No!" shouted Vial. "They've misled you! There aren't any *bambinos* in the Pacific! We forbid you any demonstration! Come back on shore this minute!"

And we laughed, because it is good to laugh, and because one laughs easily in a climate where there is a real long, hot summer with soft breezes, and leisure to state with confidence: "To-morrow, and the next day too, we'll have days no different from this when the blue and golden moments glide by, days when 'suspended time stands still', merciful days where shadows come from a drawn curtain, a closed door, or leafy trees, and not from an overcast sky."

I took special notice to-day of the way in which my friends and neighbours of the bay leave me after the eleven o'clock bathe, which ends towards half-past twelve. None of the men present asked Vial, "Are you coming?" None of them suggested to him, "I'll drop you at your door, it's on my way." They knew that Vial would be lunching with me. On the days when I don't know whether Vial is lunching with me or not, they know all the same. None of them, when they went off in one direction or another towards the horns of the crescent-shaped beach, thought of stopping and looking back to see whether Vial were coming. But none of them wanted to cause me pain or irritation by saying to Vial, "Oh yes, of course, you're staying here."

Gloomily, Vial watched them depart. On other days it was only their presence that made him gloomy. A secret, well guarded by its custodians, hermetically sealed, will keep without harm, and without result. But Hélène Clément had spoken and the honourable peace was at an end. The violated secret scattered its seeds, the seeds of a secret divulged. Vial now acted like a man who has been wakened in the middle of the night, robbed of his clothes and pushed out of his own house. And I feel neither refreshed nor irritated, but a little disillusioned by my solitude. Twenty-four hours, a few words: only twenty-four more hours are needed, and a few other words, and time will resume its limpid course. There are some fortunate rivers whose silent flow is troubled only by one gurgle, a

sob in the water marking the place where a submerged stone lies.

"As soon as we've had coffee, Vial, there's something I want to say to you."

For the meal itself is given over to the filtered sunlight, to the relaxation that comes from the cool bathe
and lingers after it, and to the begging animals. The
spots of sunlight shift slightly over the cloth; the
youngest she-cat, on hind-legs against an earthenware
jar, explored with her paw its garlanded paunch of
pink clay.

But no sooner had coffee been served, than it so
happened that the nursery-gardener appeared and had
it with us.

Afterwards I steered him through the vines to
where the clipped hedging of impoverished shrubs
requires reinforcing with new plants if it is to provide
a protective windbreak for my vines and young peach
trees against the mistral. Then my afternoon nap,
too long postponed, began to reassert its rights. Let
anyone who has not experienced a longing for sleep on
a glorious hot day in Provence, cast the first stone!
It penetrates through one's forehead, drains the
colour from one's eyes, and the whole body obeys it
with the involuntarily tremors of a dreaming animal.
And what had become of Vial! Gone, dissolved in the
flamboyant torpor, drawn into the shadow of a pine
or an espalier as he passed.

It was half-past three. In this climate, what care or
duty can stand out against the need to sleep, to enter
a cool abyss in the burning centre of the day?

Vial returned, like an overdue bill. He came back

without returning, for he had done no more than drop my neighbours opposite at their house, my peaceful neighbours, who live remote among their beautifully set-out vines that keep the building speculators at a respectful distance. He returned, dressed in white, as evening fell, and as he was pretending to turn his five-horse-power car round and be off again, I called out sternly: "Well, Vial? A glass of home-made liqueur?"

He came up the path without saying a word, and as he made his way through the blue evening air, it seemed to me that this man with his head bent, the sudden chill in the air, the ordinary little house where a woman, her face difficult to make out, waited on the threshold, and the red lamp set on the balustrade, were horribly sad. Horribly, horribly sad. Let me set down these words and repeat them; let the gilded night receive them.

Horrible sad, abandoned, still warm but scarcely alive, silent because of I know not what shame. The gilded night is about to end. Between the serried stars glides a pallor that is already no longer the perfect blue of August midnights. But all is still velvet, nocturnal warmth, and the rediscovered pleasure of being awake in the midst of sleep. It is the deepest hour of the night, and not far from me my familiar creatures seem lifeless save for the rise and fall of their flanks.

Horribly sad, unbearably sad, sad enough to contract one's throat and dry up one's saliva, to inspire the lowest instincts of terror and self-protection—for was there not a single, imponderable instant, when I

would have stoned the man who was coming towards
me, when I would have pushed my empty wheelbarrow
and thrown the rake and spade in his path? The bitch,
who never growls, growled out of subtle contagion,
and Vial called to her "But it's Vial!" as he would
have called "Friend!" in a moment of danger.

When we entered the low, pink and blue living-
room, everything came right again. I can never keep
up the dramatic spell of fear, the sentimental illusion of
it, for more than a moment. Vial smiled, his lip curled
against his teeth, dazzled by the two lit lamps, for the
days are getting shorter and the window held now
only an aquarium of green sky, pierced by two or three
stars throbbing irregularly.

"Oh, how comforting those lamps are," sighed Vial.

He stretched out his hands to them as though to a
fire in the hearth.

"The cigarettes are in the blue pot. You've had
to-day's newspapers?"

"Yes, do you want them?"

"Oh, I, you know, newspapers. . . . It was only to
have news about the forest fires."

"Have there been some forest fires?"

"There always are in August."

He sat down like a visitor, lit a cigarette as if he
were on the stage, while I reached under the table for
the flat brick on which, with the help of a little lead
hammer—a souvenir from the press of *Le Matin*,—I
crack open kernels of the umbrella pine.

The jobs I don't like are those that need patience.
It takes patience to write a book, and also to win over
a man when he's feeling savage, to mend worn linen

too and to sort the raisins for a plum cake. I would never have made either a good cook or a good wife, and I nearly always cut string instead of untying knots.

Vial, sitting sideways, looked as though he were caught in a trap, and I began patiently to untie the knots in the string.

"Does this noise of pine-nuts cracking irritate you? If you're thirsty, the water-cooler is outside there, and the lemons."

"I know, thank you."

He was vexed with me for being so unusually attentive. Stealthily he took note of the fact that I had put on new Catalan espadrilles, and that I was ceremonially garbed in an immaculate cotton frock, one of those red, white and yellow negresses' robes that brighten the coast and follow the law of the sun rather than that of fashion. While I was eating my nuts I opened an illustrated magazine; Vial smoked without stopping and followed intently, through the window, the flight of bats against the background of gradually darkening sky. A block of sea, petrified and black under the sky, could still be distinguished from the land. The evening hydroplane, preceded by the low-pitched F that it draws from the wind, appeared carrying its red lantern among the paler lights. The she-cat, outside, mewed to be let in, rearing itself against the lowered mosquito-screen and scratching it delicately like a harp-player. But Vial laughed to see her and she disappeared, after fixing him with a cold stare.

"She doesn't like me," sighed Vial. "Yet I'd stoop

to anything to win her. If she knew it, d'you think she'd like me a little better?"

"You may be sure she does know."

This answer satisfied him for a few minutes, then he sought a different reassurance, a different answer.

"Aren't the Luc-Albert Moreaus, or Segonzac the Ravishing One, or at least somebody or other, supposed to be coming to say good night to you, on their way back from dinner at *Le Commerce* this evening? I thought I'd understood . . . Or perhaps it was you who were to have gone there . . . Aren't the Carcos . . . ? I can't remember exactly . . ."

I looked at him sideways.

"The painters are usually asleep at this hour. Since when have I received people in the evening? The Carcos are at Toulon."

"Oh, good. . . ."

Secretly tired, he compromised by half reclining. His cheek pressed against the cushions of the divan, he automatically clutched the corner of one of them, his eyes closed and his hand clenched, as though hanging on to a reef. What ought to be done with this flotsam! What a problem! And then, there's the awkwardness of our respective ages, think of it, the difference between them! If that's what you're thinking, how far removed you are from what actually happens in such a case! We older women don't even think of it. We certainly think of it less than does a mature man, although it's entirely in order for him to flaunt his fondness for tender young girls. If people realised how lightheartedly we accept and forget our "duty as elders"! We think of it just enough to arm

ourselves with coquetry, to pay attention to our health
and our adornment, and to assume pleasing wiles—
things incidentally that are also demanded of young
women. No, no, when I write "what a problem!",
I don't want some reader later on to misunderstand.
It would be wrong to imagine "us older women"
trembling and aghast in the light of our short future,
suppliants before the man we love and overwhelmed
by awareness of our position. We're not nearly so
aware as people think, thank God, and much more
gallant and simple. What is a difference of fifteen years
to us? It takes more than a trifle like that to frighten
us, just when we're getting to the stage of reasoning
about such matters with a wisdom—or a folly—
worthy of the other sex. I couldn't have chosen a better
moment for affirming this than now, when here I am
as sensible as can be, more or less a widow, tender to
my memories and determined to remain so.

When I write "we women", I don't include her who
gave me the gift of carrying the years as lightly as an
apple tree does its flowers. Listen to her telling me of
a wedding dinner.

*"In the evening, a big dinner for eighty-six people, that's
enough to show it was appalling, isn't it? If I'd died that day
it would have been from those four and a half hours of
wretched food, which I hardly touched. I was paid a lot of
compliments there. On my get-up? Certainly not, on my youth-
fulness. Seventy-five . . . it's not true, is it? Must one really
soon give up being young?"* No, no, of course not, don't
give it up yet—I've never known you anything but
young, your death saves you from growing old and
even from dying, you who are always with me. The

last period of your youth, that of your seventy-fifth year, continues still. You are wearing a big straw hat that lived out of doors all the year round; beneath that cloche of finely plaited straw twinkle your roving, changeable, insatiable grey eyes, that take on a curious lozenge shape when you are uneasy or on the alert. No more eyebrows than the Mona Lisa, and a nose, my goodness, a nose. . . . "We have an ugly nose" you used to say, looking at me, in more or less the same tone of voice as: "We have a ravishing garden." And a voice, a walk. . . . When people who didn't know you heard your little, young-girl's step on the stairs and your crazy way of opening a door, they would turn round and remain speechless at seeing you disguised as a little old lady. *"Must one really give up being young?"* I don't see that that would serve any purpose, or even be seemly. Look, my dear, at this helpless youth, circling round a still-born hope that he can't leave alone, and see how traditional and hard to move he seems to us! What would you have done with him, what ought I to do with him?

Yes, what a problem! That body hanging on to a corner of a cushion, his modest bearing in his sad state, his careful dissembling of it—all that lying on my divan, what a problem! Yet another vampire, without a doubt. That is my name for those who lay claim to my pity. They ask nothing. "Only leave me there, in the dark!"

Time hung heavy as it ticked by in silence. I read, then stopped reading. On any other day I might have supposed that Vial was asleep, for sometimes my friends do fall asleep on my divan, after a long day's fishing or driving or bathing, or even work, a day that renders them speechless and charms them to sleep on the spot. This one wasn't asleep. He was unhappy. Suffering is the first disguise, the first offensive, of the vampire. Vial, far from happy, was pretending to rest, and I felt stirring at the root of my being the one who now inhabits me, lighter on my heart than I was once in her womb. I know very well they are hers, these stirrings of pity I don't care for. But she didn't like them either: *"Old Champion's niece is better. It will be a stiff job for your brother to pull her through and, as I couldn't do anything more for the moment, I've been begging on her behalf once again. But I haven't got the art of doing that gracefully, because the minute I come across people who won't give anything and only want to feather their own nests, I get red in the face and am more likely to slang them than flatter them.*

"As for your cat, I go every afternoon to the Little House to give her some warm milk and make a blaze of shavings for her. When I haven't got anything I cook her an egg. I don't do it because it amuses me, heavens above, but I can never rest if I think a child or an animal is hungry. So I do what will set my mind at rest: you know my egotism."

That's the word! Was there ever anyone cleverer at choosing her words? Egotism. That egotism led her from door to door, calling out that she couldn't bear the winter cold that was freezing some poor children in a room with no fire. She couldn't bear it when a dog that had been scalded by his master, the pork butcher, could find no other remedy than to howl and writhe outside a closed and indifferent door.

My very dear, can you see, from the summit of this

night designed for a vigil, warmer and more enriched
with gold than a velvet tent, can you see my trouble?
What would you have done in my place? You know
where those attacks of an egotism that I inherited
from you have already led me? They led you to that
material ruin in which you foundered, having given
everything away. But to have no money any longer is
only one step on the way to destitution. Undefeated
by your final poverty, you became more clear and
shining the more it ate into you. But it's by no means
certain that, at the sight of that half-reclining body,
you wouldn't have made a little detour, lifting the
edge of your skirt as you used when you passed a
puddle. In your honour I at last decided to show my
strength to the young man who was shamming sleep
because he was stiff with apprehension.

"Are you asleep, Vial?"

He was awake, so he didn't start.

"A bit dazed," he said, sitting up.

He smoothed his hair back, straightened his open
shirt and flannel jacket and retied his *espadrilles*. I
thought how long his nose was, and that he had that
pinched look of being caught between two swing
doors that you see on people who think they are
hiding their vexations. I didn't hurry him, well knowing that when a man isn't sure of his shirt buttons or
his shoelaces, it's not the moment to drag him into
psychology.

"Vial, I told you this morning that I had something
to say to you."

He bent his head with an oriental majesty.

"Very well, then. Vial, my dear, what wonderful

weather! Listen to the hydroplane with its F note, the gentle wind high up between the east and the north, breathe in the pine and mint from the little salt marsh; its fragrance is scratching at the gate like a cat!"

Vial raised his eyelids, which he had kept lowered, his whole face opened with surprise, revealing all his masculine good faith, and I felt myself strong in the presence of this creature full of innocence, unversed in the artifice of speech.

"Have you seen the grapes on the vines, Vial? Have you noticed that the clusters are already huge and turning blue, so close-set that a wasp couldn't squeeze between them? D'you realise that we shall have to gather them before the fifteenth of September? What d'you bet that the season'll run its course before the storms get past *Les Maures*, where the mountain is gathering them together like balloons at the end of a string? It's raining in Paris, Vial. It's raining at Biarritz and Deauville too. Everything is mildewy in Brittany, and the Dauphiné is covered with mushrooms. Only Provence . . ."

While I was speaking he narrowed his eyes and his whole face hardened. A living being is an endless occupation. All that this one now surrendered to me was a wary glimpse of himself. Being a man, he fears irony. Despising melancholy, he was now merely perplexed, and stiff.

"D'you understand me, Vial? It's a very lovely time of the year that I'm spending here. It's also, I assure you, a very lovely time of my life. D'you like these months that you're spending here?"

By imperceptible movements Vial's features again

became the face of a brave man to whom the power to use his courage has been restored.

"No," he answered, "I don't like them. I wouldn't exchange them for anything in the world, but I don't like them. Not only have I hardly done a stroke of work all this time, but worse still I'm not happy."

"I thought you were designing an 'ensemble' for . . ."

"For the _Quatre Quartiers_. Yes I am. My models are ready. It's a big job. Living-rooms, bedrooms, dining-room, the whole house. I'm using every penny I've got, and even a bit more, to make my models in wood and metal. But if I succeed, it means I shall be the director of the modern furniture workshops at the _Quatre Quartiers_."

"You've never told me so much about it before."

"That's true. You're not much interested in modern furnishing."

"At least I'm interested in what concerns my friends."

Vial settled himself on the divan with the movement of a horseman getting a grip on his saddle.

"Madame, I don't for a moment flatter myself that I'm your friend. You have scores of friends like me that you greet familiarly in your cheerful holiday mood."

"You're modest."

"I'm clear-sighted. It's not very difficult."

He spoke in an even, respectful voice, with an open look on his face, while his large and certainly beautiful eyes looked frankly either into mine or at some other part of my person.

"It's true, Vial, that I'm more familiar than quick

to make friends. But where friendship is concerned, is there so much hurry? We should have become friends . . . later on. I know you very little."

He made a quick gesture with his hand to efface my words.

"Oh Madame, please, please!"

"You called me Colette yesterday."

"In front of people, yes, so as to seem one of the anonymous crowd. If you paid any attention to me you'd know that I've never once called you by your name when we were alone. And we've been alone together very often, since the first of July."

"Yes, I know."

"By the tone of those three words, Madame, I see we're arriving at the matter than concerns us."

"At the matter that concerns you."

"Anything that's disagreeable to you, Madame, certainly does concern me more than anything."

At that point we stopped for a moment, for the unexpected rapidity of our replies had brought us to what sounded like a quarrel.

"Gently, Vial, gently! Now, shoulders steady, and then all of a sudden . . ."

He smiled because I did.

"Accused people sometimes decide to 'come clean' because they know they'll be condemned. And then they'll talk about their crime as easily as about their first love, or the baptism of their little sister—it doesn't matter what."

He cracked the joints of his clasped fingers between his knees and questioned me urgently.

"Madame, what do you want of me? Or rather,

what don't you want? I'm certain already that you're going to ask me the thing that will be hardest for me, and that I'll do whatever you want."

How men's nobility, even when it consists of nothing but words, pulls us up short! The feminine tendency to dress a man up as a hero, when he talks of sacrificing his emotional comfort, is still very strong in me.

"Good. So there won't be any difficulty. Hélène Clément . . ."

"No, Madame, not Hélène Clément."

"What d'you mean, not Hélène Clément?"

"What I say, Madame. Not Hélène Clément. Enough of Hélène Clément. Something else."

"But do try and understand me. Listen. You don't even know . . . She came yesterday and I had no difficulty in finding out for certain . . ."

"Bravo, Madame! That does credit to your perspicacity. You found out for certain? I'm delighted. Let's speak no more of it."

A sharp little light shone in Vial's eyes, and he stared at me impertinently. When he saw that I was going to get angry, he placed his hands on mine.

"No, Madame, let's speak no more of it. You want to let me know that Hélène Clément loves me, that my indifference distresses her, that I ought to feel pity and even love for that 'beautiful healthy young girl'— Géraldy's expression—and marry her? Good. I know it. It's finished. Let's speak no more of it."

I withdrew my hands.

"Oh, if you take it like that, Vial . . ."

"Yes, Madame, I take it like that and, what's much more, I reproach you for having dragged the name of this young girl into our conversation. You had a reason for doing so? What reason? Say it! Say it, then! You take an interest in this young girl? You know her well? You've undertaken to be responsible for the future and even for the happiness of a frail creature who's hardly twenty-six years old? Are you so fond of her? Are you her friend? Answer, Madame, answer more quickly! Why don't you answer more quickly? Because I don't give you time? It doesn't take long, Madame, to answer 'yes' whole-heartedly to all my questions, and as a rule you're prompt. You don't like Hélène Clément and, if you'll forgive the expression, you don't care a damn about her happiness, which in any case doesn't in the least concern you. Don't get angry, it's settled, it's finished. *Ouf!* I'd be glad of a glass of lemonade and I'll prepare one for you. Don't move."

He poured out our drinks and added: "Apart from that I repeat that I'll do what you like. I'm listening."

"I'm sorry. It was you who spoke of 'coming clean'."

"It would be unpardonable of me, Madame, to prevent you from continuing your rhapsody on the beauties of summer."

Ah, if I had but felt a beating of the heart, a prophetic coldness of the hands, those preliminary symptoms of distress in every part of the body! If I know myself aright, it was then and not later that I regretted the absence between us of that supreme intruder, desire. If it had been present I should, I think, have

been easily able to draw from it the meaning of our
meeting that evening, the spice and the danger which
it lacked. It seemed to me also too obvious that Vial
wanted to stress the contrast between the young companion of yesterday, the "my little Vial" who was one
of a band of summer comrades, and the completely
self-contained lover.

"I've already noticed, Vial, that we don't need many
words to understand each other."

It was an ambiguous compliment, and went deeper
than I had meant.

"Truly?" said Vial. "Truly? You really think that?
To how many men in your life have you said something like that? Perhaps you've only said it to me? I
must say I haven't noticed a sign of it in any of your
books . . . no, not in any. What you've just said is
quite unlike that contempt for love that in reading you
one is always slightly aware of in your love for love.
It isn't a thing that you would have said to one of the
men who . . ."

"We're not concerned with my books here, Vial."

I couldn't hide from him the jealous discourage-
ment, the unjust hostility that seizes me when I realise
that people expect to find me true to life in the pages
of my novels.

"You must allow me the right to hide myself in
them, even if it's only in the 'stolen letter' manner.
Now let's get back to what does concern us."

"Nothing concerns both of us together, Madame,
and that makes me very sad. You've taken it into your
head to plant a third person between yourself and me.
Send her away and we shall be alone."

"But it's because I promised her . . ."

Vial threw up his hands, so dark against his white cuffs.

"So that's what it is! You promised her! Promised what? Frankly, Madame, what are you up to in this?"

"Not so loud, Vial, Divine's sleeping in the hut in the vineyard. The little Clément girl told me that last year, in this very place, you exchanged words that led her to believe . . ."

"Very likely," said Vial. "This year it's different, that's all."

"That's not very gallant."

Vial turned towards me abruptly.

"Why isn't it? What would not be gallant would be if, having changed my own mind, I hadn't warned her. I've neither run away with a minor nor slept with a decent girl. Is that all you have to reproach me with? Was it in honour of that insipid creature that you sang your hymn in praise of summer? Was it with an eye to Hélène Clément's happiness that you decided—for you have decided it—to banish me? Why do you choose to send away the one who cares most for you and understands you best? Is that the promise you made to Hélène Clément? In the name of what did she get it out of you? Of the 'correct thing'? Or of the difference in our ages? She's quite capable of it!" he cried with a note of harsh gaiety in his voice.

With a nod of denial I gave him my most affectionate look. Poor Vial, what a confession! So it was he who was thinking, was he, of the difference in our ages? What a confession of torments, of silent debates!

"Must I confess it to you, Vial? I never think about differences in ages."

"Never? What, never?"

"What I mean is . . . I just don't think about it. Any more than about the opinion of imbeciles. And that isn't the promise I gave Hélène. Vial"—I laid the flat of my hand, as I often do with him, on his swelling chest—"is it true then that you've become attached to me?"

He lowered his eyelids and compressed his lips.

"You've become attached to me in spite, as you say, of the difference in our ages. If there were no other barrier between us, I assure you that wouldn't count for much in my eyes."

With his chin he made a very slight shy movement towards my hand spread on his chest, and promptly replied.

"I'm not asking you anything. I shan't even ask you what it is you call another barrier. I'm even astonished to hear you speaking so . . . so naturally of . . . of these things that concern you."

"It's very necessary to speak of them, Vial. What I made plain to Hélène Clément was only—and in any case very vaguely—that I wasn't an obstacle between you and her, and that I never should be one."

Vial's expression changed, and with the back of his arm he pushed my hand away from his chest.

"That beats all," he cried in a choking voice. "What a lack of awareness! To associate yourself . . . To put yourself on the same plane as she! To pose as a generous rival! Rival of whom? Why not of a shopgirl? It's incredible! You, Madame, you! To put yourself, to behave like an ordinary woman, you that I'd like to see, oh, I don't know . . ."

With his raised hand he assigned me a lofty niche in the air, a kind of pedestal, and I interrupted him with an irony that pained me.

"Vial, let me stay among the living for a bit longer. I'm quite comfortable here."

"Oh, Madame. . . ."

Vial gazed at me, speechless with reproach and grief. With a swift movement he leant his cheek against my bare upper arm and closed his eyes.

"Among the living?" he repeated. "Why the ashes, even the ashes of these arms would be warmer than any living flesh. They would remain an encircling necklace still."

I had no need to break the contact, for he himself broke it immediately, to make me pleased with him. I was pleased, and I nodded approvingly at him as I watched him. I saw weariness, and a blue-black film creeping over his cheeks because of the lateness of the hour. Thirty-five or six, neither ugly, nor unwholesome, nor wicked. I was being swallowed up by the airless night during the passage of those hours when all the world is asleep, and there emanated from this lightly clad and emotionally overwrought youth an odour of amorous midnight that little by little began to make me feel sad.

"What keeps you going, Vial, apart from me? You understand what I mean?"

"Very little keeps me going, Madame, very little— and you."

"That isn't much of a portion for you."

"That's for me to say."

I got angry.

"But, you obstinate brute, where do you think you're going, where were you off to without saying a word, now that you've made a habit of me?"

"As a matter of fact I haven't the slightest idea," he answered carelessly. "The truth is I've thought of it as little as possible. Sometimes in Paris, when you hadn't time to see me, I used to think . . ."

He smiled to himself, already absorbed by the longing to describe himself, to come out into the open.

"I used to think: 'So much the better, if I don't see her I'll get more quickly over the longing to see her. I've only got to be patient, and when I go back to her she'll suddenly be sixty or seventy and then life will become possible and even agreeable again.' "

"I see. And then?"

"And then? And then when I went back to see you it happened to be a day when all your demons were awake, and you'd put on powder, made up your eyes, slipped into a new frock and could talk of nothing but travels, the theatre and playing *Chéri* on tour, planting vines and peach trees and buying a little car. And I had to begin all over again. It's the same here too," he ended, more slowly.

Throughout the silence that followed, nothing from outside disturbed the immobility of all things. In the beam from the lamp the cat, lying in the hollow of the *chaise-longue* on the terrace, announced the approach of the dew by rolling herself into a ball and the creaking of the wicker resounded as though under a vault.

Vial questioned me with his eyes as if it were my
turn to say something. But what could I have added to
his deep, melancholy contentment? No doubt he
knew I was moved. I was. I made only one sign, which
he interpreted as meaning, "Go on . . ." and an almost
feminine expression, full of seduction, passed over his
features, as if his whole, brown, masculine face were
going to break up and reveal a dazzling countenance;
but it did not last. It was only the flash of a semblance
of triumph, of a spark of happiness. Come now, I
must act quickly and rather sternly, to undeceive this
decent man. Swifter than I, he plunged in deeper.

"Madame," he went on, restraining himself from
speaking with heat, "I haven't much more to say to
you. I never have had much to say to you. No one is
more devoid of second thoughts—I might almost add
'of desires'—than I."

"Yes, there's me."

"Forgive me, but I can't believe you. You invited
me this evening . . ."

"Yesterday evening."

He passed his hand over his cheek and became embarrassed to find it stubbly.

"Oh, how late it is! You invited me yesterday evening, and yesterday morning you . . . summoned me.
Was it only to talk to me about the little Clément girl?
And of the fact that you felt it your duty to get rid
of me?"

"Yes. . . ."

I hesitated, and he rebelled.

"What else is there, Madame? I beg you not to get
it into your head that I must be managed and treated

carefully. I'd rather confess to you that I'm not even unhappy. Truly not. Up to now I've felt like someone carrying on his person something very fragile. Every day I breathed again, 'Still nothing broken to-day!' There never would have been anything broken, Madame, if the rather heavy and perhaps not very well-intentioned hand of an outsider . . ."

"Oh come now, leave the child alone."

As soon as I heard my words I was ashamed of them. I still feel ashamed of them as I write them down. They were the words, and the tone of voice, of a mawkish rival, of a perfidious stepmother. It was the inveterate homage, the mean acquiescence which comes out of us when man solicits it, man, that luxury, that choice game, the most rare male. Vial imprudently glittered with joy, like a fragment of glass in the moonlight.

"But I do leave her alone, Madame, I've never wanted to do anything else! I'm not asking anything of anyone, *I*'m not! I'm so nice, so easy. . . . Listen, Madame, if you were to suggest to me, you yourself, that I should change, that . . . that I should improve my lot, I should be capable of crying 'Rubbish!' and even '*Vade retro!*' "

And he burst out laughing—all by himself. He had overshot his capacity. A grown man can hardly ever play the urchin with impunity. Besides, in order to be attractive when he acts caddishly, he must have a deeply engrained evil streak, the gift of improvisation, or at least the light touch that some mediocre Satans achieve—all virtues which extreme youth has no difficulty in making up for.

Was the honest Vial, by making himself cheap like
a little middle-class girl going on the streets out of
despair, perhaps trying, in order to please me, to
conform to a type of man he had discovered in three
hundred pages of mine, in which I celebrate slightly
dishonourable masculine immunities? If so, it might
have made me smile. But like the night, I was beginning to throw off langour and would soon emerge
from the shadows. Through the door came a coldness
bred of the clash between a young breeze and yesterday's air, heated by our two bodies. The flagstone of
the threshold gleamed as though under rain, and the
ragged ghost of the big eucalyptus gradually loomed
up against the sky again.

Vial was mistakenly hoping that his passivity would
win the day. That's not an uncommon tactic with
men—rather the reverse. Vial belongs to a category of
lovers that, in the course of my amorous life, I have
merely glimpsed from a distance of my own choosing.
He must be a bit dull all day long, but when dusk falls
he shines and becomes apt for love, pleasing during
love-making as young peasants are, and workmen in
the flower of their youth. I could see him, I could indeed, as if I were there.

Vial swiftly put a woollen scarf round my shoulders,
though I had not shivered.

"Is that all right? You'll be warm enough? The
day will soon be here, Madame. It can be my witness
that I never hoped to see it dawn alone with you in
your house. Let me at least be proud of that, if not
happy. I often sin through pride, as happens with
people of lowly origin who are disgusted with the

milieu to which they were born. Disgusted . . . that's it, I was born disgusted. My war-time comrades joked about my disgust for ordinary women and common-place adventures. A prince couldn't be more disgusted than I. It's comic, isn't it?"

"No," I said absently.

"If you knew," he went on in a lower tone, "it's only here that I've lived through such long days. Of all the things in you that have helped me, none is so precious as that colour that your even temper gives to the days, the savour they acquire by gliding over you. In spite of a kind of mannishness, a hail-fellow-well-met manner which you only put on. . . ."

I did not interrupt him. A dull blue light lay on his forehead and the hollows of his cheeks, the orange-coloured lamps grew red under the insinuating pro-gress of the blue. In the enclosed garden a bird freed itself from the night with a cry so long, so divorced from melody, that it gave me the illusion of tearing myself from sleep. Dark in his white garments, curled up in the hollow of the divan, Vial still belonged lazily to the night, and in order to see him better I made use of a former self of mine who awoke in me with the day, a self that enjoyed physical exchanges and was expert at discerning promise in the shape of a body. The nakedness of the daily bathe had made the contours of this particular body familiar to me: the Egyptian shoulders, the strong cylindrical neck, and above all the lustre, the rare and mysterious signs that confer on certain men a grade in the voluptuous hierarchy, in the animal aristocracy. So—feeling I hadn't much time—I hastened to breathe in through all my pores the warmth that came to me from a forbidden spectacle "*since it was nothing but straw . . .*"

"When one is fortunate enough to return from the war in such a commonplace way, with two scars on the arm, all one asks for afterwards is to live fully and work hard. But my father . . ."

What is it that he lacks, then? What disturbance, what drama of gestation, of growth? He has nothing in common with the people I've known, whose stammerings have communicated themselves to me when I've held them in my arms and looked down at them.

"To want everything, to be aware of everything, at the bottom of one's heart to lay claim to everything, is a great misfortune for a young man who is obliged to live in a mediocre way, and who didn't know that one day he would have the luck to be listened to by you."

Yes. But there is no chance that his appearance, his effort to join me, even his suffering could convey to me the torture of the seed beneath the soil, the torment of the plant in such a hurry to flower, since that is its duty, that it lacerates itself in the process. I've known, then lost, beings who swore—it was their way of testifying to my power—that they would perish if I did not release them from themselves, that they would never blossom if I refused them their only climate: my presence. But this one had already flowered, and lost his flowers, more than once.

". . . and I'm not ashamed to let you see that I'm more astonished and poorer in memories than in life had just begun for me. . . ."

Yes. But it hasn't just begun for you. That's only a

manner of speaking. You can't deceive me about that, even by playing on your innocence. We older women, when our last, valiant combats are over, are generally concerned only with the worst or the best; there's no great merit in discerning that you are neither the one nor the other. I'm thinking of my future, whose hours may be counted. If I were to enter the lists again, that future would be entirely given over to burning truths, to bitternesses more cruel than all—or else to duels where each side wants to outstrip the other in pride. You are marked out for an easier destiny, Vial, than trying to outstrip me in pride.

"Dear Valère Vial!"

I hoped that this cry would release me from that privileged place where it was for me to choose whether to wound or to help.

"I'm here, Madame, I'm here! In fact that is my greatest crime."

Stiff from his long watch, he got up and stretched, obliterating all his angles. His beautiful summer livery, polished and brown, looked soiled on the cheeks by the stiff stubble that pierced the skin. The brilliant white of his eyes was less clear than yesterday. Without a night's sleep, or any attention, what was my face looking like? I think of it to-day, I didn't think of it yesterday. All I thought of was to seal, with a wound or an embrace, the night that was over at last. A couple absorbed in each other doesn't know what a brief conversation is. How endless are those discussions in which those who are not true lovers flounder!

The sour scent of some peaches, forgotten in a

bowl, reminded me of their existence. I bit into one
and suddenly I was hungry and thirsty again for the
round material world, crammed with savours: in a
few moments boiling milk, black coffee, and the butter
lying at the bottom of the well would fulfil their healing office.

"Dear Valère Vial, you diverted me from what I
had begun to say to you a moment . . ."—I playfully
pointed out to him one of the last stars, pale yellow,
which had stopped its scintillating dance—"a moment
ago."

"You have only to go on, Madame. Or to begin
again, I'm still here."

Was this sincere friendship, or a pretence of friendship? From the pleasure that I derived from his
friendly voice, I realised that this sleepless night had
told on my strength.

"Vial, I wanted to talk to you as to an affectionate
human being—if there are human beings that are
affectionate."

My reservation came at the right moment: Vial
jibbed at the word spurned by all lovers, and his look
took back the trust he had reposed in me.

"I told you that I was spending here a beautiful
time of the year, but above all a beautiful time of my
life. This is a fairly recent state of affairs, as my
friends know."

He remained silent, as if dried up.

"So that I don't always feel very sure of myself in
this new state. Sometimes I am forced to ask myself—
when all of a sudden I go in for great activity, such as
spring-cleaning, insensate gardening, or a move—if

it's because of this new lightness or the remains of old fever. D'you understand?"

He nodded "yes", but showed me the face of a stranger, and it didn't occur to me then that he might be suffering.

"To make a clean sweep, to build up once more, to be born again has never been too much for me. But to-day it's no longer a question of making a clean sweep, it's a question of beginning something I have never done. So understand, Vial, that this is the first time since I was sixteen that I'm going to have to live— or even die—without my life or death depending on love. It's so extraordinary. You can't know. You have time."

Vial, unconcern stamped all over him, stubborn from head to foot, silently refused to understand or help me out. I felt very tired, ready to recoil before the crimson invasion that was rising from the sea, but I also wanted to end this night honourably—the word suggested itself to me and I couldn't get rid of it.

"You see, in future my sadness, if I'm sad, and my gaiety, if I'm gay, must exist without the motive which has been all they needed for thirty years: love. I've nearly got there. It's prodigious. It's so prodigious. When a woman has just given birth to a child, a reflex action sometimes makes her cry out again on waking from her first sleep after deliverance. And I, you see, still have the reflex of love, I forget that I have put aside the fruit I once produced. I don't struggle against it, Vial. Sometimes I cry inside myself: "Oh dear, provided He's still there!" and sometimes: 'Oh dear, provided He's no longer there!"

"Who?" asked Vial, naïvely.

I began to laugh, and patted the beautiful chest that his open shirt exposed to the morning wind and to my hand—my hand that is older than I, though at that hour I must certainly have looked my age.

"No one, Vial, no one. No one any longer. But I am not dead, far from it, nor insensible. I can be hurt. You could hurt me. You're not the kind of man to be satisfied with that?"

A long hand with thin fingers, swift as a paw, seized mine.

"I could still make do with that," he muttered.

It was only a passing threat. I was grateful to Vial for such an avowal, I relished the slightly outrageous form, the direct and obvious source of it. I withdrew my hand gently, shrugged my shoulders and tried to make him ashamed, as I would a child.

"Oh, Vial! What end do you think would await us if I listened to you?"

"What end?" he repeated. "Oh, of course. Why, your end—or mine. I admit," he added complacently, "yes, I admit there were times when I shouldn't have minded if you'd died."

I found no answer to so time-honoured a wish. A slight quiver of his eyeballs, a vague laugh showed me that Vial might still be thinking of acting the desperate lover and I began to be pettily afraid lest anyone should discover this dishevelled boy on my doorstep. There was no time to be lost, the day was upon us, the first whirring swallows were encircling the roof. Only a long Chinese junk of clouds, thick red-violet in colour and anchored flush with the horizon, delayed the first fire of dawn. With a great roll of hollow, singing thunder, a wagon on the coast road proclaimed that it was transporting empty barrels. Vial turned up the collar of his white jacket round his yesterday's beard and the brown face that sleeplessness and starvation were turning green. He shifted his weight from one foot to the other, as though he were trampling snow, and he gazed for a long time at the sea, my house and two empty seats on the terrace.

"Well then . . . *au revoir*, Madame."

"*Au revoir*, dear Vial. You . . . I shan't see you at lunch-time?"

He took this for an excess of hostile precaution, and was hurt.

"No. Nor to-morrow. I must go to Moustier-Sainte-Marie, and from there to some little places strung along about two hundred kilometres of the coast. To buy some Provençal counterpanes for my shop in Paris, and some Varages plates that I've been told about."

"Yes. But this isn't an 'eternal farewell'! We'll see each other again, Vial?"

"As soon as I can, Madame."

He seemed pleased to have answered so well in so few words, and I let him go. His little car started up discreetly in the deep white dust of the dry road. Then the cat appeared, like a fairy, and I went into the kitchen to light the fire without waiting for Divine, for I was trembling with cold and all I felt was an urgent need to soak myself in a very hot, vinegary, aromatic bath, a bath like those in which one takes refuge in Paris, on black winter mornings.

We settlers, scattered along the coast, enjoy impromptu dinners because they bring us together for an hour or two but do not violate the peace of our dwellings, the privacy of our summer life, which does not include afternoon reunions or five o'clock teas. The protocol of the season demands that a sudden unanimous whim, rather than friendly planning, should regulate our relations. If we get an invitation for a week ahead we are hesitant and evasive: "Oh, I don't know if I'm free. It just happens that the Gignoux boy has to take us to La Seyne. . . ." Or else we're working, or we're "just" planning a picnic in the forest, to feed off poached game.

As a rule it happens that a single voice, we don't know whose in advance, expresses our desire for brief sociability. It may be that of the Great Dédé, or Dorny's little nasal pipe, or the ravenous yawn of Daragnès sighing: "How empty I feel . . ." And it can't happen until half-past seven has struck on the bulbous belfry, until the last spark of the setting sun, dancing on the bellies of the siphons, is reflected in Segonzac's green, sorcerer's eyes, and until a vague smell of bread comes from the pink façades along the quay, warmer than the cooling air. Only then does a nonchalant voice speak up. "I wonder what there is to eat at *La Lyonnaise's*?"

No one has moved, yet the reply comes, surprisingly precise. "Nothing. Tomatoes, and the local ham."

"We've got a big Bologna sausage and some fine gorgonzola," murmurs another sweet voice, which belongs to the violonist Morhange. "But that wouldn't be enough for everyone."

"And I suppose *my* soup of *my* onions, *gratiné*, is just so much goat dung?" cries Thérèse Dorny, or Suzanne Villeboeuf.

At this point Segonzac rises to his feet, doffing his ancient felt hat: "My good sirs, my good ladies, could it be that a jaunt as far as my house would frighten you off? I'm only a simple peasant, I have what I have but, faith of a churl, I have my heart on my hand and my hand everywhere."

While the Ravishing One is still at his favourite game of imitations, silent feet, shod with *espadrilles*, have been running hither and thither until, loaded with local ham, tomatoes and peaches, cheeses, almond tarts, sausages shaped like a club, long breads that we hug as if they were stolen children, and a hot soup-tureen tied up in a napkin, we take to the rutty hill road in two or three cars. The exercise is familiar to us: twenty minutes later a table set up under a wattle roof offers us a feast, and the green moonlight of old starboard lights, hung high in the branches, streams unctuously over the convex leaves of the magnolias.

That is how we were yesterday evening, at the top of the hill. The inlet of sea, away below, kept a milky clarity that no longer came from the sky. We made out the motionless lights of the port and their trembling reflections. Above our heads, between two torches, swung a long bunch of ripening grapes, and one of us picked a green one.

"The vintage will be early, but scanty."

"My farmer says that we shall make ten hectos, all the same," states Segonzac with pride. "What about you, Colette?"

"I'm reckoning on a third of the crop, it hasn't rained enough and mine are very old vines: eighteen hundred to two thousand."

"Two thousand what?"

"Litres; but I only have half of it for myself."

"God's death, my good girl, you'll turn into a wine merchant!"

"A thousand litres!" sighed Suzanne Villeboeuf, quite overcome, as if she were condemned to drink the lot.

She was wearing a frock with sprays of flowers on a black ground, peasant stuff from Italy, which she had cut in the style of old Provence, and no one could explain why she looked as though she were disguised as a gipsy.

The air smelt of eucalyptus and over-ripe peaches. Silkworm moths and the delicate butterflies of the gooseberry bushes crackled as they got burnt in the shades of the electric lights. Hélène Clément patiently rescued the least hurt on the end of a pickle-fork, and then out of pity gave them to the cat.

"Oh, a shooting star!"

"It fell on Saint-Raphael."

We had finished eating, and almost finished talking. A big jug of ordinary greenish glass, with a jutting navel, was passed lazily round the table and tilted to fill our glasses again with a good wine from Cavalaire, a young wine with an after-taste of cedar wood, whose warm vapour awakened a few wasps. Our sociability, now that it was satisfied, was on the point of giving place, according to the swing of the pendulum, to our unsociability. The painters, tired out with sun, would have given way to a childlike torpor, but their wives, who had rested after lunch in a harem-like peace, turned longing eyes towards the bay and hummed under their breath.

"After all," one of them risked, "it's only a quarter to ten."

"Waltz, pretty maidens!" sang a timid soprano, and then stopped short.

"If Carco were here . . ." said another voice.

"Carco doesn't dance. What we need is Vial."

Whereupon there fell a very short silence and Luc-Albert Moreau, afraid I might be hurt, cried: "It's true, it's true, we need Vial! But since he isn't here, you see . . . Well, he isn't here, that's all!"

"He's preparing his white exhibition, and his sale of household articles," said Thérèse contemptuously. As she was trying to rent an "amusing" little *boutique,* she envied Vial his Parisian shop.

"He's at Vaison, behind Avignon," said Hélène Clément.

My friends looked at her sternly.

She kept her eyes down and went on feeding grilled moths to the black cat on her knee, that looked like a conger eel.

"That's enough to make it burst," Morhange pointed out to her vindictively. "Isn't it, Madame Colette?"

"Oh, no, why? They're fat, and roasted. Naturally I

wouldn't grill butterflies for cats on purpose, but you can't prevent silkworm moths from flying at the electric lights."

"Nor women from going dancing," sighed a tall landscape painter, getting up. "Come on, let's go and have a hop at Pastecchi's. But we'll go home early?"

One of the young women threw out a "Yes!" as piercing as the whinny of a mare, headlights ranged over the vines, striking here and there a vine-stock of quicksilver, a dog white as salt, a livid terrified rose-bush. Seeing Luc-Albert grovelling like a suppliant before an ancient and obstinate little car, Thérèse Dorny threw at him in passing, "Won't your stove draw to-night?", and our laughter descended the hill, carried by silent cars in neutral gear.

As we drew nearer to the sea, the bay became more thickly starred. I felt the bare arm of Hélène Clément against my bare arm. Since the departure of Vial, I had only seen her on the quay, in the bookshop, at market time, at lemonade time, and never alone. In the first days of the week she had shown me an eagerness, a deference as much as to say: "Well? Well? What have you been doing? What news?" to which I had answered nothing. She was, I thought, resigned, and was thinking—but how could I have thought so?—of other things. Her bare arm, in the shadow, gave under mine.

"Madame Colette, you know," whispered Hélène, "I only know it by a post-card."

"Know what, my child?"

"And it's a post-card from my mother, who's with

father at Vaison, staying with my grandmother Clément," she went on, passing over my question. "Our families know each other. But I thought I couldn't say it just now . . . that it was better . . . I wasn't able to consult you about it before dinner."

I pressed the bare arm, cool as the evening.

"It was better."

And I was astonished that she should know so well what is better, what is less good, I admired her face full of plans and hopes for events, arrivals, embarkations.

When night has fallen, reducing the sea to its language of lapping waves, noises like sucking lips, and obscure gnawings between the bellies of the moored boats, the marine immensity to a little black wall, low and vertical against the sky, the outrageous blue and gold of the day to the lights of the jetty, trade to the two cafés and a little night-prowling bazaar, then we discover that our port is just a little port. As we passed by, a foreign yacht, in a good position flush with the quay, was shamelessly displaying its brasses, its electricity, its bridge of West Indian wood, its dining table surrounded by men naked to the waist and women in low frocks with great ropes of pearls, its immaculate waiters. We stopped to contemplate the magnificent ark that the sea had brought and that the sea would take away, when those people had thrown overboard their last fruit-peeling and decked the water with their floating newspapers.

"Hi, you there, chuck us some cigarettes," a down-at-heel boy called to them.

One of the passengers on view turned round to eye

the child perched on the gangway, and did not answer.

"Hi, all of you, what time do you make love? If it's late, I'm afraid I won't be able to wait till then."

He fled, rewarded by our laughter.

A hundred metres further on, in the crook of the jetty, Pastecchi has his dance-hall and bar. It's a good corner, sheltered from the wind. It's beautiful because its view embraces at the same time a section of imprisoned sea, the *tartanes* adorned with painted stripes and the flat houses on their splayed bases, of tender lilac and dove-pink.

An exhausted little man, who looks lazy but rarely rests, stands guard over the bareness of a rectangular hall, as though he had been ordered to keep any decoration away from it. There's not a festoon to be seen on the walls, nor a bunch of flowers on the corner of the counter, no fresh colour anywhere, not even a paper frill round the electric bulbs. As in a mortuary chapel for the poor, it is on the catafalque that a display of flowers and superfluity is amassed. What I call the catafalque is the ancient mechanical piano, stricken in years and black as an old tail-coat. But there isn't one of its panels that doesn't frame, in wistaria and blue ribbons, Venice, the Tyrol, a lake in moonlight, or Cadiz, painted in lifelike colours. It swallows, through a slit of a mouth edged with brass, counters worth twenty centimes, and gives them back a hundredfold in metallic polkas and *javas* made of lustreless tin, full of big gaps of consumptive-sounding silences. It is a hollow music, of such a dismal severity that we couldn't bear it without dancers. As soon as the first measures precipitate into the coffer a rhythmical shower of old coins, bits of glass and lead combs, a couple, two couples, ten couples of dancers revolve obediently, and when you don't hear hemp soles sliding, you're aware of the silky rustle of bare feet.

When I write dancers, I refer to men and not girls. At the Jetty these are a negligible minority. Pretty, bold, and with shaven necks, they learn from the tourist the chic of sunburnt legs and the incomparable scarf. But when a "foreign woman" comes to the dance in the evening in *espadrilles*, the local girls wear patent leather slippers on their bare feet.

We all crowd together on the wobbly wooden benches, round a cracked marble table. Even so some young workmen from the factory and two sailors, in order to make room for us, have to move back their tom-cat loins and their glasses of *pastis*. Hélène Clément clamped her bare shoulder, her hip and her long leg against a young sea animal, polished like precious wood, with the confidence of a girl who had never found herself in the middle of a deserted road, three steps away from a silent, motionless, unknown man with swinging arms. Some men take for impudence, in Hélène, what is only persistent purity. She got up promptly and went off to waltz in the arms of a blue sailor, who danced as the youths do here, that is to say without speaking, clasping his partner in a close and impersonal embrace and holding high his face, which revealed nothing.

Around this beautiful couple turned, under the cruel glare of the execrable lighting, a few habitués of the coast: two Swedes—husband and wife, brother and sister?—all pale red from ankles to hair, some massive Czechs, their bodies hardly hewn out of the block, two or three new-style German women, thin, half-naked, swarthy and hot on the eye—so many coloured stains against a dark background of shirtless adolescents in thin black sweaters tight round the neck, sailors blue as the night, and ruddy-bronze, thickset stevedores of *tartanes,* light on their feet, heroes of the dance. They were waltzing with each other under the impure gaze of a public come a long way to see them. Two friends, like as twins in their stature, their slender feet and the similarity of their smiles, who hadn't condescended the whole summer to invite a "bitch from Paris", came to rest near us, accepted from the great Dédé, who admired them, a bottle of fizzy drink, answered, to an indiscreet question, "We two dance together because the girls don't dance well enough", and went off to entwine their arms and mingle their knees again.

A frantic brunette with straight hair, in a yellow fichu, come just as she was, in a car, from a neighbouring shore, was rubbing stomachs with an aloof workman who, though he held her by the loins, seemed not to see her. A charmer of a dark young man, in a torn shirt of grey flannelette, who seemed riveted to another young man, delicate, empty and immaterial, the whiter because of a red silk handkerchief, tied tight high up round his neck, under the ear, threw us glances of defiance as he passed, and a hammer-shaped mulatto—huge shoulders and a waist that could have fitted into a garter—carried against his heart, feet off the ground, a child almost asleep with so much gyrating, who let his head flop and his arms hang limp.

No other noise beyond the clink of coins, crockery and dominoes, all blended together with that of the mechanical piano. One doesn't come to the Jetty to talk, nor even to get drunk. At the Jetty one dances.

The open windows let in the smell of the melon rinds floating on the water of the port; between two parts of a tango, a long sigh announced that a wave, born far out at sea, had just died within a few paces of us.

The young women with me watched the male couples circling. In their excessive attention I could read both their mistrust of these enigmas and their attraction for them. The great Dédé, narrowing his green eyes, his head on one side, was calmly enjoying himself, and saying from time to time, "It's pretty—it's pretty. It's already spoilt, but it's pretty. Next summer they'll dance because Volterra will be watching them dance."

The little gipsy Villebœuf spun round in her turn like the corolla of a flower. We refrained from speaking, dazed by the whirling and the unpleasant light. The draught of the dance drove against the ceiling a veil of smoke that tried, at every pause, to come down again, and I remember that I was content hardly to think, to accept the battered music, that year's little white wine that became tepid as soon as it was poured out, and the increasing heat heavy with smells. Coarse tobacco triumphed, then gave way to green mint, which was effaced by a rough, musty smell of clothes soaked in brine; but a brown body, sheathed in a little knitted, sleeveless jerkin, smelt as it passed of sandal wood, and the swing-door of the cellar gave out fumes of wine dripping on sand. The good shoulder of a friend propped me up and I was waiting until satiety should give me the strength and desire to get up and return to my tiny kingdom, to the anxious cats, the vines, the black mulberry trees. I was waiting for that . . . a minute more and I'll go . . . only that truly. . . .

"It's no good," said a young cinnamon-coloured woman," what we needed this evening was Vial."

"Take me home, Hélène," I said, getting up. "You know very well that I can't drive in the dark."

I remember that she drove me very gently, avoiding the stones and the holes which are familiar to us, and that she dipped her headlights on arriving so that they would light up the path. On the way she talked of the dance, the temperature, and the little local roads in a tone so restrained, so heavy with solicitude and attentiveness that, when she ventured to ask me in a voice full of feeling, "Isn't it three years that they've left these two holes unfilled?" I was tempted to answer: "No thank you, Hélène, I don't need any cupping-glasses this evening, and the bromide potion is unnecessary."

I could tell she was full of zeal and attentions, as though she had felt on me a painless bruise and spilt blood that I didn't feel myself. It was to thank her that I said to her, when she ran to open my gate that doesn't fasten, while I was putting down my aged Brabançon bitch: "You were superb this evening, Hélène, even better than last month."

She drew herself up with pride in front of the headlights.

"Was I? I feel it's true, Madame Colette. And it isn't over! It's only beginning. I think . . ."

She lifted her finger like a great warring angel, upright in the middle of a white halo. Putting mystery aside, she turned her head towards the "Thimble".

"Really?" I said vaguely, and hurried along the path with a sort of repugnance for everything that wasn't my own lair, the welcome of the creatures, the cool sheets, a cavern of silence. But Hélène rushed forward and seized me by the elbow, and all I could then see in front of us was two enormous ink-blue shadows that crept along flat on the ground, were broken at the foot of the façade, scaled it vertically and gesticulated on the roof.

"Madame, it's crazy and stupid, but without the slightest reason I have a . . a presentiment . . . like a great hope . . . Madame, I'm very devoted to you, you know . . . Madame, you understand everything. . . ."

Her long shadow gave my shorter shadow an incoherent kiss that fell somewhere into the air, and she left me, running.

"I've just been sorting some papers in dear papa's desk. I found there all the letters that I wrote to him from the Maison Dubois after my operation, and all the telegrams you sent him during the period when I couldn't write to him. He had kept everything; how moved I was! But, you'll say to me, it's quite natural that he should have kept all that. Not so natural, believe me; you'll see. When I returned from the two or three short trips I made to Paris to see you, before his death, I found my dear Colette a shadow of himself and hardly eating. Ah, what a child! What a pity he should have loved me so much! It was his love for me that destroyed, one after another, all those splendid abilities he had for literature and the sciences. He preferred to think only of me, to torment himself for me, and that was what I found inexcusable. So great a love! What frivolity! And as for my side of it, how can you expect me to get over the loss of so tender a friend?"

A gentle rain has been falling for two hours, and is about to stop. Already the heavenly bodies are disputing the end of the afternoon. A rainbow has tried to bridge the bay; broken off half-way over by a solid mass of stormy clouds, it brandishes in the air the marvellous fragment of a semicircular arch whose colours blend in death. Facing it the sun, with its spokes of divergent rays, descends slowly towards the sea. The waxing moon, white in the broad daylight, frolics between wisps of airy clouds. It is the

first rain of the summer. What good will it do the
vintage? None. The grapes are almost ripe. When
I try them at the first dawn they're cold, bedewed
and elastic, spurting sweet juice as you bite into
them.

The pines filter the shower as it slackens; in spite of
the scent of them, of the wet orange trees and the
sulphurous seaweed smoking along the shore, this
water from heaven bestows on Provence a smell of
mist, of undergrowth, of September, of the provinces
in the centre of France. What a great rarity to find a
misty horizon below my window! I see the landscape
trembling, as though through rising tears. There's
novelty and a sweet reversal of the normal in everything, even to the gesture of my handwriting, a
gesture that for so long has belonged to the night.
But I had to celebrate the rain in my own way—and
besides, this week I have no taste except for what I
don't much like.

The shower drifts away to *Les Maures*. All the
denizens of my house celebrate the end of the bad
weather. A hymn of thanksgiving, besprinkled with
"Mercy me!", "Lord preserve us!" and "Jesus, I
surrender!" arises from the kitchen. The she-cat, on
the edge of a puddle, gathers drops of water in the
hollow of her little cat's hand and watches them
trickling down, just like any young girl playing with
her necklace. But the tom-cat, who had forgotten rain,
hasn't yet recognised it. He sits on the threshold and
studies it, shivers running over his body. A vague
smile begins to appear on his pure and stupid face.
If the bad weather were to continue, he would be sure

to cry, all beaming with complacency, "I've understood! I remember! It's raining." As for that big
boneless gawk, his daughter—whom we call the
Tiny One in memory of the time when she was only
six weeks old—whether it rains or shines, she goes
hunting. She is heavy with murders, and standoffish.
Her fur, lighter coloured than it should be with blue
blood like hers, is like white frost on a slate roof. A
heady scent of bird's blood, trodden grass and warm
lofts follows her, and her mother avoids her as though
she were a fox.

I have only to remain eight days without writing,
and my hand forgets how to write. For the last eight
or ten days—precisely since the departure of Vial—I
have had a lot to do; or it would be truer to say, I've
done a great deal. I've deepened and cleaned out the
party-ditch that drains the superfluous waters of
winter. "I tell you, it isn't the season for that!"
Divine reproaches me. Then there was weeding, hard
work when the earth is hard, and the rinsing of the
wicker-covered demijohns. I've also oiled the shears
for the vintage and rubbed them with emery-paper.
Three days of great heat kept us near the sea, and in
the sea, enjoying the cool weight of its short swell.
A hoar frost of fine salt covered our arms and legs
before they were barely dry. But although the sun
attacks and overcomes us, we feel he is no longer
aiming at us from the same quarters of the sky. At
dawn, in front of my window, it is no longer the
eucalyptus that divides the first segment of the sun
rising from the sea, it is a pine next to the eucalyptus,
How many of us see the day appear? The ageing of

the sun, which each morning shortens its course,
takes place in private. It is enough for my Parisian
comrades, and for the Parisians who are not my
comrades, that when it sets it should fill the sky for a
long time, taking possession of the afternoon and
crowning it.

Shall I tell of the two excursions that saw us,
numerous and gay, happy to set off and happier to
return? I love the old Provençal villages clinging to
the crests of their hills. Ruins there are dry, whole-
some, stripped of grass and green mildew, and only
the geranium-ivy with its pink flowers hangs from the
black gaping ear of a tower. But in summer I quickly
tire of penetrating inland; I am thirsty for the sea,
for the unwavering horizontal join, blue against blue.

I think that's all. Do you think it isn't much?
Perhaps you're right. Perhaps I'm incapable of portraying for you what I myself don't clearly distinguish.
Sometimes I take for silence what is a great internal
rustling, weariness and happiness, and what draws a
smile from me is nearly always a regret. Since Vial's
departure I strive hard to attain serenity, and naturally
I only bring to the task materials of sound origin,
some taken from a still recent past, others from my
present which is becoming clear, and the best I beg
from you, my very dear. The result is that my serenity,
which I've acquired without having any natural
tendency, has the look—not so much artificial as pains-
taking—of something that's been worked at too conscientiously. I would exhort it, "Come on now, get
drunk! Stagger a bit!" if I were certain that it would be
merry in its cups.

When Vial was here, during two consecutive summers, his presence . . . No, if I were to speak of him I
shouldn't do it well. I leave it to you, my subtle
companion, to praise a Vial you have not known.

*"I leave you to go and play chess with my little wool-seller.
You know him. It's that ugly little fat man who sells buttons
and darning-wool sadly all day long, and never says a word.
But would you believe it, he plays a subtle game of chess.
We play in his back-shop where there is a stove, an armchair
he brings forward for me, and on the window, that gives on
to a little court, two pots of very beautiful geraniums,
those incomprehensible geraniums that you find in poor
dwellings and in the houses of level-crossing keepers. I've
never been able to have any like them, I who give them
air and pure water, and pander to their every whim. So I go
very often to play chess with my little wool-seller. He waits
for me faithfully. He asks me each time if I want a cup of
tea, because I am 'a lady' and tea is a distinguished drink.
We play and I think of what is imprisoned in that fat little
man. Who will ever know? It makes me curious. But I have
to resign myself to never knowing, though I'm very glad to
feel sure there's something, and to be the only one to know it."*

Flair, instinct for hidden treasure. Like a diviner she
went straight to what shines only in secret, water which
languishes far from the light, the dormant seam,
hearts from which every chance of blossoming has
been withdrawn. She listened to the liquid sob, the
long underground whisper, the sigh.

She would never have asked brutally: "So, Vial,
you've become attached to me?" Such words wither
everything. Have I regrets, then? That ordinary
youth? There are no distinctions in love. Does one ask

a hero: "Little wool-seller, do you love me?" Does
one push things to their conclusion with such haste
as that? When, as a little girl, I used to get up at about
seven o'clock, astonished to find the sun still low, the
swallows still perched in a line on the gutter and the
nut-tree gatherng its icy shadow beneath it, I would
hear my mother cry: "Seven o'clock! My goodness,
how late it is!" Shall I never catch her up, then?
Free, and flying high, she says of constant, exclusive
love, "What frivolity!" and then scorns to explain
herself at length. It's for me to understand. I do what
I can. It's high time for me to approach her by
some other means than through my professed liking
for jobs without urgency or greatness, and to get
beyond what we irreverent children used once upon
a time to call "the cult of the little blue saucepan".
She would not be satisfied—nor am I—to know that
I often gaze at and caress everything that passes
through my hands. At other times I find I am being
pushed out of my own self and forced to grant a large
measure of hospitality to those who, having handed
on to me their place on earth, are only in appearance
submerged by death. The wave of fury that rises in
me and masters me like a pleasure of the senses: that
is my father, his white Italian hand closing round the
sprung dagger that never left him, and feeling for its
blades. My father, again, is the jealousy that made
me, in other days, so awkward. I tread obediently in
the footsteps, stopped for ever, that traced their way
from the garden path to the cellar, from the cellar to
the pump, from the pump to the big armchair full of
cushions, opened books and papers. On that trodden

path, lit by a low, sweeping sunbeam, the first of the
day, I hope to learn why one must never put a single
question to the little wool-seller—I mean to say Vial,
but it is the same perfect lover—why the true name of
love, that suppresses and condemns everything around
it, is "frivolity".

I remember one evening—it will soon be eight days
ago and it was the evening when Hélène brought me
back from the dance—when I thought I had left on
the road, in the arms of Hélène's shadow clasping the
shoulders of my shadow, a relic that was not exactly
meant for her but which it was important that I
should get rid of—old reflexes, servitudes, harmless
aberrations.

When Hélène had gone I opened the door of the
enclosure giving on to the vineyard, and called my
creatures: "My creatures!" They rushed up, bathed in
moonlight, impregnated with the odours that they get
from the beads of resin and the hairy mints, deified by
the night, and once again I was amazed that, being so
beautiful and so free, masters of themselves and of
those night hours, they should prefer to come running
at my voice.

Then I settled the bitch in an open drawer of the
chest-of-drawers and installed in front of me, on my
bed, the low table with its rubber *sabots*, adjusted the
porcelain shade whose green light answered, from
afar, the red lamp that Vial lit in the "Thimble".

"You are the starboard light, and I the port side,"
jested Vial.

"Yes," I answered, "we never look towards each
other."

Then I took the top off the softened gold nib of one of my fountain-pens, the one that runs best, and I did not write. I let the night, the long night, minister to me. The next night, and the next, will be longer still. Nights, like bodies, stretch themselves as the fever of summer leaves them. And I said to myself that, as far as the décor was concerned—the black night, the solitude, the friendly animals, a great circle of fields and sea all around—I should be thenceforward like the woman I have described many a time, that solitary upright woman like a sad rose which carries itself the more proudly for having been stripped of its leaves. But I no longer trust in what I look like, having known the time when, while I was painting this lonely creature, I would go to show my lie, page by page, to a man, asking him, "Have I lied well?" And I would laugh, as my forehead sought that man's shoulder, and his ear that I nibbled, for I could never get over the belief that I had lied. Nibbling the cool gristly lobe of his ear and pressing his shoulder, I laughed under my breath. "You're there, aren't you?" But already all that I held was a deceptive solidity. Why did he stay? I inspired him with confidence. He knew I could be left alone with matches, the gas, and firearms.

The gate sang. On the path, where the water shed by the sky smokes as it weds the warm earth, a young woman is walking towards my house, shaking, as she passes, the great weeping plumage of the mimosas. It is Hélène. Since Vial's departure she no longer joins us at the morning bathe where she meets, in spite of my protection, some cold faces, for I count among my friends some beings of a redoubtable

simplicity, who are bad at understanding the sound
of words because their task is to hear the passage of
thoughts.

Hélène is soon leaving for Paris. When I announced
this news, only the little voice of Morhange answered
me. "Ah, so much the better, that gawk! I don't like
her, she isn't good."

I pressed for the reason of such a lively antipathy.

"No, she isn't good," said Morhange. "And the
proof is that I don't like her."

With evening a great wind arose. It has dried the
rain, carrying away the clouds, swollen like big soft
water-skins, bringers of benign humidity. It's blowing
from the north, telling of dryness, of distant snow, of a
tense, invisible season already installed up there on
the Alps.

The animals sit and gravely watch it endlessly passing beyond the black window. Perhaps they are
thinking of winter. This is the first evening when we've
gathered in a closer circle. The cats were waiting for
me under the penthouse of reeds when I got in. I had
dined with my neighbours opposite, a young couple
who are building their nest with religious gravity.
They are still so thrilled with their new possessions
that I hurry to leave them alone, so that when I've
gone they can count over again the treasures they have
acquired, and timidly talk of the things they quiver
with longing to possess. After dinner in their house an
empty cradle is brought into the low hall with its ceiling of great beams; this is filled with a little child as

round and pink as a radish, made to fit it. Then I
know that it is ten o'clock, and I go home.

Hélène did not stay long this afternoon. She came
to tell me that she was taking the road, as she puts it,
in her five-horse-power car, with a friend who can
take turns with her at the wheel and change a tyre.

"Vial never leaves Paris, Madame Colette. He's
working like a dog at his big undertaking for the
Quatre Quartiers. . . . I have my spies," she added.

"Not too many spies, Hélène, not too many spies."

"Don't be afraid! My spies means father, and he's
helping Vial with little tips. Vial will need father, next
winter, if the Ministry doesn't fall, because father's a
school-friend of the Minister's. The important thing
is that the *Quatre Quartier* should make Vial director of
their workshops before the Ministry falls."

She shook hands with me and a word of passion
escaped her: "Ah, Madame, I should so love to help
him!"

She will get Vial. I've tried, these last days, to urge
on her prudence in pursuit—"dignity" and not
"prudence" was what I had in mind—and a different
strategical style. But she swept my advice aside with
a wide gesture of her bare arm, and tossed her head
with great confident tosses. So it was quite evident
that I knew nothing about it. She has a way that is
tender and proud of saying to me, "Don't be afraid!"
For two pins she would add, "Now that you're no
longer in the neighbourhood of Vial, I can deal
with him."

For two or three weeks past I've sometimes taken
pride in the thought that, if I wanted to do harm, I

could. "I could still make do with that," Vial had said, craftily. We were both boasting. Hélène will get Vial and that will be right—my hand nearly wrote: and it will serve her right?

It's blowing outside, but without a drop of rain. I shall lose the rest of my pears in it, but the laden vines laugh at the mistral. *"I wonder whether you've inherited my love for tempests and all the disasters of nature?"* wrote my mother to me. No. The wind, as a rule, chills my thoughts, turning me away from the present and back along the one-way street of the past. But this evening the present does not link up comfortably with my past. Since Vial left I have once again to be patient, to go forward without looking back, and only face-about deliberately, in six months, or three weeks. What, so many precautions? Yes, so many precautions, and dread of all haste, and a slow chemistry; I must cherish the sources of my memories.

One day I shall find myself savouring the love in my past, and I shall be astonished at the great troubles, the battles, the feasts, the solitudes. Bitter April, with its feverish wind, its bees caught on the sticky brown buds, its scent of apricot trees in flower will bring the spring itself to salute me, just as it was when it burst into my life, dancing, weeping, mad and wounded by its own thorns. But perhaps I shall think: "I've had better. I've had Vial."

You will be astonished: "What, that little man, who said three words and went away? Really, that little man, to dare to compare him with . . ." It's not a thing one can argue about. When one praises the beauty of one of her daughters to a mother, she smiles to herself because she thinks it is the ugly one who is the prettiest. I'm not singing Vial's praises in any lyrical vein, I merely regret him. Yes, I regret him. The need to exalt him will only come when I begin to regret him less. He'll come down to earth again —when my memory has finished its capricious work, that often removes a monster's hump or horn, effaces a mountain and respects a straw, an antenna, a reflection—he'll come down and take his place in the depths to which love, that superficial froth, does not always have access.

Then I shall think of him, telling myself once again that I let him go, that I gave Vial to a young woman with a gesture which undoubtedly had a wonderful air of ostentation and recklessness. Already, if I reread what I wrote nearly three weeks ago, I find I painted Vial badly there, with a precision which impoverishes his outline. During these past days I've thought a lot about Vial. To-day I'm thinking much more about myself, since I'm regretting him. O dear Man, our difficult friendship is still unsure of itself, thank heaven!

Let me cry once more, "Thank heaven!" my very dear mother. It's done, now I'll be quiet. It's for you to bid me be silent again. So speak on the verge of death, speak in the name of your inflexible standards, in the name of the unique virtue that you called "true elegance of behaviour".

"*All right then, I deceived you, in order to have peace. Old Josephine is not sleeping in the little house. I sleep there alone. Spare me, all of you! Don't come and tell me, you and your brother, stories of burglars and wicked tramps. As far as nocturnal visitors are concerned, there's only one that must cross my threshold now, as you well know. Give me a dog, if you want. Yes, a dog, I'll agree to that. But don't compel me to be shut up with someone at night! I've reached the point where I can't bear to have a human being sleeping in my house, when it's a human being I haven't made myself. My own code of morals won't let me. It's the final return to single life when you refuse to have any longer in your house, especially if it's a small one, an unmade bed, a pail of slops, an individual—man or woman—walking about in a night-shirt. Ugh! No, no, no more company at night, no more strangers breathing, no more of that humiliation of waking up simultaneously! I prefer to die, it's more seemly.*

"And having made my choice, I'm all for coquetry. You remember that, at the time of my operation, I had two big bed-jackets made for me, in white flannel? I've just had a single one made out of the two of them. What for? Why, to be buried in. It has a hood, trimmed with lace all round, real thread lace—you know how it gives me the creeps to touch cotton lace. The same lace on the sleeves and round the collar (there's a collar). Precautions of this kind are part of my feeling for what's right and proper. I'm already upset enough that Victor Considérant should have felt obliged to give my sister-in-law Caro a magnificent ebony coffin, with silver handles, that he had had made to measure for his own wife. But she was so swollen she couldn't get into it. That silly creature, Caro, appalled by such a present, gave it to her charwoman. Why didn't she give it to me? I like luxury, and can't you see how comfortably lodged I should have been in it? Don't let this letter upset you, it comes when it should and is what it ought to be.

How many more games of chess have I still got before me?

For I still play, from time to time, with my little wool-seller.
Nothing is changed, except that now it's I who play less well
than he, and who lose. When I become too incapable and
clumsy, I shall give that up as I give up everything else, out of
decency."

It's good to learn such a lesson of behaviour. What
breeding! I think I hear her, and pull myself together.
Fly, my favourite! Don't reappear until you have
become unrecognisable. Jump through the window and,
as you touch the ground, change, blossom, fly, resound. . . . You could deceive me twenty times before
you imposed on her, but all the same serve your
sentence, slough off your skin. When you return to me
I must be able to give you, as my mother did, your
name of "pink cactus" or some other flame-shaped
flower that uncloses painfully, the name you will
acquire when you have been exorcised.

She wrote the letter that I have just copied with a
hand that was still free. Her pointed nibs scratched the
paper—she always made a great noise as she wrote.
That letter, written to protect herself—and us—from
imprisonment, illness and immodesty, must have filled
her room with a scraping noise like the frantic feet of
an insect. Yet at the end of the lines the last words
turn down, drawn by an invisible slope. Brave though
she was, she is afraid. She is thinking with dread of
being dependent, of dependence in general; and she
takes the trouble to warn me. The next day in another
letter she delicately changed the subject to relieve my
mind: a charming story of some wild oats, whose

beards, thrusting to right or left, foretell the weather,
follows her previous admonitions. She grows enthu-
siastic in relating the visit of her grand-daughter G,
during one of her bad fits of drowsiness, when she
was drugged with *digitalis*.

"*Eight years old, her black locks all tangled, for she had
run to bring me a rose. She remained on the threshold of my
room, as alarmed by my waking as by my sleep. I shall see
nothing before my death as beautiful as that shy child, who
wanted to cry and held out a rose.*" Between us two, which
is the better writer, she or I? Does it not resound to
high heaven that it is she?

Dawn comes, the wind falls. From yesterday's rain,
in the shade, a new perfume is born; or is it I who am
once again going to discover the world and apply new
senses to it? It's not too much to be born and to create
each day. The bronze-coloured hand that runs, stops,
crosses out and starts again, is cold with emotion,
cold with a youthful emotion. For hadn't niggardly
love wanted to fill my cupped hands one last time with
a little shrivelled treasure? In future I shall gather
nothing except by armfuls. Great armfuls of wind, of
coloured atoms, of generous emptiness that I shall
dump down proudly on the threshing floor.

Dawn comes. Everyone knows that no demon can
stand its approach, its pallor, its bluish gliding; but
no one ever speaks of the translucent demons that
amorously attend upon it. A blue of farewells, choked
and spread by the mist, billows fog-like into the room.
I need but little sleep; for many weeks now I have
made do with a siesta. When the desire for sleep
seizes me again, I shall sleep the brutal sleep of a

drunkard. I have only to wait for the return of a
rhythm interrupted for a time. Only to wait, to
wait. . . . That is a lesson learnt in a good school,
where true elegance of manners is taught also, the
supreme elegance of knowing how to diminish.

I learn it from you, to whom I turn without ceasing.
A letter, the last, came quickly after the laughing
epistle about the ebony coffin. Ah, let me hide under
that last letter the image that I don't want to see: a
head half vanquished, turning its dry neck impatiently
from side to side on the pillow, like a poor goat
tethered too short. No doubt my mother wrote that
last letter to assure me that she no longer felt any
obligation to use our language. Two pencilled sheets
have on them nothing more than apparently joyful
signs, arrows emerging from an embryo word, little
rays, "yes, yes" together, and a single "she danced",
very clear. Lower down she had written "my treasure"
—her name for me when our separations had lasted a
long time and she was longing to see me again. But
this time I feel a scruple in claiming for myself so
burning a word. It has a place among strokes, swallow-
like interweavings, plant-like convolutions—all messages from a hand that was trying to transmit to me a
new alphabet or the sketch of some ground-plan
envisaged at dawn under rays that would never attain
the sad zenith. So that instead of a confused delirium,
I see in that letter one of those haunted landscapes
where, to puzzle you, a face lies hidden among the
leaves, an arm in the fork of a tree, a body under a
cluster of rock.

The cold blue has crept into my bedroom, trailing

after it a very faint tinge of flesh colour that clouds it.
It is the dawn, wrested from the night, drenched and
chill. The same hour to-morrow will find me cutting
the first grapes of the vintage. The day after to-
morrow, even before this hour, I want . . . Not so
fast! Not so fast! That deep hunger for the moment
which gives birth to the day must learn patience: the
ambiguous friend who leapt through the window is
still wandering about. He did not put off his shape as
he touched the ground. He has not had time enough
to perfect himself. But I only have to help him and lo!
he will turn into a quickset hedge, spindrift, meteors,
an open and unending book, a cluster of grapes, a
ship, an oasis. . . .

The Blue Lantern

I

WE should not be unreasonably perturbed when our
precious senses become dulled with age. I say " we ",
but I am the text of my own sermon. My chief concern is
lest I should mistake the true nature of a condition which
has come upon me gradually. It can be given a name: it
keeps me in a state of vigilance, of uncertainty, ready to
accept whatever may fall to my lot. The prospect gives
rise to little that is reassuring, but I have no choice.

More than once of late, turning my eyes from my book
or my blue-tinted writing paper towards the superb
quadrangle that I am privileged to view from my window, I have thought 'The children in the Garden are not
nearly so noisy this year,' and a moment later found
myself finding fault with the door bell, the telephone, and
the whole orchestral gamut of the radio for becoming
progressively fainter. As for the china lamp—not the blue
lantern that burns by day and night, of course, but the
pretty one with flowers and arabesques painted on it—I
was for ever scolding it unjustly: ' What can this wretched
thing have been eating to make it so heavy?' Discoveries, ever more discoveries! Things always explain
themselves in the long run. Instead, then, of landing on
new islands of discovery, is my course set for the open
sea where there is no sound other than that of the lonely

heart-beat comparable to the pounding of the surf? Rest assured, nothing is decaying, it is I who am drifting. . . . The open sea, but not the wilderness. The discovery that there is no wilderness! That in itself is enough to sustain me in triumphing over my afflictions.

Four years have gone by since *L'Etoile Vesper* was published; years that sped speedily enough as they must when the mornings are all alike and the evenings are spent in a kind of glass retort, with some unpredictable little incident at the centre, like a kernel. I was honest when I called *L'Etoile Vesper* my last book. I have come to see that it is as difficult to stop writing as it is uncomfortable to go on. Beneath my blue lantern, my life-line grows ever shorter and shorter, my physical torment ever more persistent. Yet how many changes of scene—other than on foot—are still permitted me! Uriage in '46, Geneva and the Beaujolais in '47, Provence, albeit against doctor's orders, in '48. From my seat in a car or a wheel-chair, I proudly compiled a census of the landscapes, streams and shores I have rediscovered. 'After all, I can still visit these.' Visit! Yes, in a manner of speaking and, above all, of experience. During the final infirmity of her life, Anna de Noailles saw more cities, hills and oceans than I, against the backcloth of her perpetually lowered blinds.

I wanted this book to be a journal; but I do not possess the knack of writing a proper journal, that is to say of stringing together, bead by bead, day after day, a rosary whose value and intrinsic lustre are relative to the writer's powers of exact observation, of assessing his own importance and that of his time. The art of selection, of noting things of mark, retaining the unusual while discarding the commonplace, has never been mine, since most of the time I am stimulated and quickened by the ordinary. There I was, vowing never to write anything again after *L'Etoile Vesper*, and now I have covered two hundred pages which are neither memoirs nor journal. Let my reader resign himself to it: this lantern of mine, burning blue day and night between the pair of red curtains, pressed close to the window like one of the butterflies that fall asleep there on a summer morning, throws no light on events significant enough to astonish him.

It is twenty years, or a little more, since Princesse Edmond de Polignac, staunch friend of music and musicians, passed sentence with a glance and a single word on the little four-legged table-desk that used to follow me from Paris to Saint-Tropez and back, taking up its position on the bed at my night's lodging. I set great store by this piece of furniture, originally contrived for me by Luc-Albert Moreau—painter, engraver, and master carpenter —so that I could write other than in a sitting posture, my feet dangling, which has always had an adverse effect on my comfort and my work.

"I have," Princesse de Polignac said to me, "a little English piece which, if enlarged, would be just right for you."

She was not mistaken. Widened, made higher, reinforced, and stripped of most of its English eighteenth-century elegance, it bestrides my divan-bed and indeed, for a quarter of a century, has gladdened both my leisure and my working hours. An adjustable desk has been let into the solid mahogany table and takes the weight of the things I turn to for relaxation from my own writing: telephone, fruit, portable radio, and bulky illustrated volumes. This contraption glides easily from the head of the bed to my feet. Including the all-purpose knife with its scorpion handle, the bunch of fountain-pens and various knick-knacks of no particular use, I have assembled on its back a fair number of good and willing servants.

All round me a litter of papers; but a litter belied by its appearance, with more often than not, to add to the confusion, a boiled chestnut, a half-eaten apple, and for the last month a seed-pod—from some exotic plant, no doubt —the capsules of which retain for a while and then expel, almost with violence, a delicate silvery follicle weighted with a tiny seed and lighter even than thistledown. One by one these feathery tufts break loose, drift up to the warm air beneath my ceiling, float there for some time before descending, and should one of them happen to be caught by the draught from the fire it yields at once, a consenting victim, and flings itself deliberately into the flames, there to perish of its own volition. I do not know the name of the plant which scatters its winged spirits abroad in this fashion, but it has no need of a label to take its place in my dunce's museum.

What has become of those whom I wanted to last for ever, firmly attached to their own lives and mine? How could I ever have conceived that Marguerite Moreno would abandon me? She was kindly treated even by fatigue, and she would laugh me to scorn in my praise

of idleness and the forty winks of a siesta. . . . But
Marguerite goes and catches cold, and succumbs within
a week. But Luc-Albert Moreau, happening to meet a
friend, exclaims cheerfully "Hullo, old chap, how
pleased I am to see you!" and dies on the spot from heart
failure. And before them Léon-Paul Fargue who, on his
death bed, grumbled about the blue of his sheets which
he had had dyed: "Far too blue . . . won't do at all."
And others there are too whom I must give up trying to
name, or even count. In my heart of hearts I blame them
for dying, calling them careless, imprudent. How could
they deprive me of their company, and so abruptly, how
could they think of doing such a thing to me! So I have
banished from sight and mind the vision of them lying
prone and lifeless for ever. Fargue turned suddenly to
stone? I'll have none of it. My Fargue is still wearing his
dusty walking-shoes, still talking, scratching the head of
his black cat, is still ringing me up, still tramping from
Lipp to Ménilmontant, and berating his bed for its too
maritime blue. . . . Marguerite Moreno's feet still shod
with static gold? Certainly not! They live in my memory
as they were, wayward, restless, vulnerable and never
tired.

My juniors in the prime of life sometimes look sternly
at me; they feel anxious. They gather the recalcitrant
fold of a shawl across my shoulder with a "You're not
feeling a draught?". No, I am not feeling chilly, I am
not feeling *that particular* draught you have in mind. My
thoughts are too out of joint for me to feel it. I have so
many reasons for avoiding what you tactfully call "the
dangerous draught". Chief among them is pain, pain
ever young and active, instigator of astonishment, of

anger, imposing its rhythm on me, provoking me
to defy it; the pain that enjoys an occasional respite
but does not want my life to end: happily I have pain.
Oh, I know perfectly well that by using the adverb
"happily" I sound affected, like someone putting on the
brave smile of an invalid! Very few invalids do remain
entirely natural, but I would not like it thought that I
am making my infirmity an occasion for sinful pride, that
I require respect and special consideration, or that it
fosters an inferiority complex, that root cause of acerbity.
I am not referring to those who pretend to be sufferers,
who are of no interest and are in any case a small
minority, nor am I alluding to a category of sufferers who
are far from reluctant when surprised or discovered in
the very act of suffering. My doctor-brother summed up
in a few words the pleasure enjoyed by such as these.
"It is," he said, "a kind of ecstasy. It's akin to scratching
the hollow of your ear with a match-stalk. Aphrodisiacal,
almost."

A prominent politician, who was lame, once confided
something to me which I had no difficulty in understanding, though at the time I was myself in excellent health.
This man of politics liked to elevate my mind to the
realm of general ideas, at least he made a good try. I
struggled to follow his line of thought, but not for very
long. I believe he would have found me mediocre all in
all had he not so enjoyed one of my books, *Break of Day*,
and had he not wished to expand (I would have said
'restrict') the scope of my life by the help of some great
idea that should serve me as, in a sense, religion, high
purpose (his phrase), inspiration. Out of malice and to
get my own back, I asked him one day whether he could

conceive of what a life laid waste by a single idea would
be like, and I was astonished by his unhesitating reply:
"Perfectly well, since all my life long, every day and
almost at every hour, I have remembered that I was
lame."

Up to the time of his untimely death he endured with
great fortitude one accident and operation after another,
and his legacy to us was a considerable corpus of learned
works entirely devoted, as had been his life, to political
matters—all, that is, save one, a story of some length, in
its way a masterpiece, a single story whose hero was a
cripple.

So, as luck will have it, I am fated to suffer pain, which
I reconcile with a gambler's spirit, my ultra-feminine
gambler's spirit, my instinct for the game of life, if you
prefer it; the Last Cat, towards the end of her life, gave
every indication by the movement of a paw, by the smile
on her face, that a trailing piece of string was still for her
a plaything, food for feline thought and illusion. Those
who surround me will never let me want for pieces of
string.

✑ II *Geneva 1946*

I am just back from Geneva, where life is brisk and not too noisy. To start with I found little resemblance between the peculiar existence of an invalid-under-treatment in the heart of a foreign town and my customary way of life, adapted over the years and so ungrudgingly to the dictates of a disease with its contrasting ups and downs, and to a beloved city where I hardly had need of pain to equip me for an imitation of the thebaic life in Egypt, with its discretionary solitude and chance sociability.

Confined to my downstairs quarters, I neither heard nor was affected by the teeming life of the Swiss capital. True enough, its roadways are well laid and its traffic largely consists of noiseless vehicles. Early in the morning a hand-cart collects the leaves and twigs from the little square. And the waste paper? Certainly not! In Geneva no litter is left lying about. The little hand-cart rolls along on two large pneumatic tyres. My window looked out on a length of embankment, a street corner, and all I could see from it were sleek automobiles gleaming like brand new pianos.

The first weeks of a prolonged treatment brought me both renewed pain and respite from it, if prostration can be regarded as a lull. I only had to recall my brief periodic visits to Geneva thirty years earlier, in a family pension where theatrical and music-hall artistes, whose purses were as modestly lined as my own, frequented a table d'hôte. A Geneva under pouring rain. My pockets were stuffed with cigarettes for the needs of others (I don't smoke), and tiny gun-metal or nickel watches costing ten francs apiece, in the days when the Swiss franc and the French were equivalent.

Back in Geneva in 1946, while timid April reluctantly approached, I looked forward to the return of some of my strength, or rather of some of my optimism—the two are really one and the same—if not the decisive killing of my pain; and also to the time when an almost exclusively physical dread would so far yield as to grant me a keener perception of the town and its inmates. Had I, then, been reduced to such straits that, to start with, the mountain of solid silver on the far side of Lac Léman appeared to me as no different from its picture postcard replicas? Believe this I must, for I regarded the towering plume of water which, spurting from the lake, remains erect and brandished aloft before constantly returning to it, as little more than a glorified toy, a blade of corn, or seed-corn at the mercy of the wind yet ever resistant. Believe it I must, for at first I could not bring myself to curb a sense of dependence and humility in front of the therapeutist who had undertaken to act in my defence.

In the first place I learnt how a patient should behave under treatment: for this my doctor friends had not prepared me. I learnt how to accustom myself to punctuality and the daily round, to the hours of visitation from an all-powerful, well-intentioned, inexorable stranger. . . . The hour of fearing a certain man, a man unknown,

although he was answering my summons. It happened to
be the hour that was highly charged with a persistent
coquetry, that called for a rose-pink petticoat, a new
ribbon in the night-dress, a freshly ironed dressing-gown.
The moment that precedes the entry of such a man with
healing powers quickens the pulse more than his maltreat-
ment of the limbs—injections, massage, pommellings,
vicarious deep-ray therapy, to which his visible presence
acts as alleviation. After the cry of agony wrung from
me or the muttered oath, I indulged in a wry laugh
seemlier than a sob, a hearty swear-word, or an indecent
joke for which the doctor made allowance. After that
I would enjoy a most agreeable conversation for a minute
or so, friendly, light-hearted, when I forgot all about
myself, and . . . " Good-bye till tomorrow, my dear
doctor ".

I had indeed forgotten my Geneva of other days, since
on my first carriage outings as the April dusk was falling,
I was utterly astonished to find that the town had un-
leashed a rush of pedestrians, cyclists, and noiseless
American cars: surprised at the concourse without
hubbub, activity without collision, haste without confusion. And—greatest surprise of all to me after six years
of confinement in the blue of a Paris cellar, with the
black-out of war and the red glow of a shaded torch—the
bright carnival of electricity! Bathed in a wealth of rosy
light, the small dwellings were transformed into a quivering, teeming thoroughfare, brimming over but well
ordered, where the shop windows displayed a congeries
of goods—lace, footwear, scents and food. I never ceased

to register surprise. What! Chocolate for the asking, and gâteaux, in pâtisseries still abundantly overflowing when all had eaten their fill! Also, for the asking, to quench my lips that are parched for it, can that be milk, MILK, pure and held in reverence, sold at every door! Milk that in Paris, following the war restrictions even for the old, is bluish and rationed drop by drop. Is it really true that all and sundry, myself included, can sit down here in a garden-restaurant or ice-cream parlour, and ask for a cup, nay, two and three cups of milk and be supplied! Permissible for anyone to drink it out of a red cup blobbed with white, or one blue as a periwinkle! Drink it, invisible yet palatable, from a large galactite goblet as milk-white as itself! Or ask for it at any hour in my hotel room, either iced and tasteless or warm and evocative of glossy udders, stain it with coffee, lace it, foaming and heated, with vanilla, with sugar and rum! It will be some time before I tire of seeing milk in shining canisters being carried by children all over the town, of surveying it as so many landmarks on my wheeled outings, left unprotected at the half-open wicket of a chalet, or balanced among the unripe cherries on the lower branch of a tree, or sitting in state on the little boundary wall under the watchful eye of a cat!

For anyone not able to dawdle along a pavement and indulge the fortuitous whims and luck of the stroller, there remain only superficial sights, cities that dwindle from view, buildings enhanced by alluring optical illusions. Not only am I determined, from now and henceforward to remain satisfied with this state of affairs, but I am stimulated by the prospect. What have I to lose? Nothing now. The very contrary. Illusions crowd thick upon me. What I take to be a hedging implement, can it really be the latest invention for making coffee! And surely that pretty object so elegantly curved that it looks the ideal prop for a climbing polygonum cannot possibly turn into a trouser-press! In this country a practical invention works wonders. For how long, I wonder, will certain shops, that modestly style themselves 'iron-mongers', be inaccessible to me? I would dearly love at least to press my nose against their windows, become intoxicated with varnished woodwork, red beechwood, enamelled iron and aluminium, so effectively does Swiss ingenuity, at the mere sight of it, stir and quicken the idea of art and harmony. On the other hand, the less said about the arty shops full of assorted trinkets the better. . . .

But no one has suggested that I turn art critic, and enumerate landscapes, pink-fleshed nudes, still lifes; and goodness knows what use I could have for an embossed leather writing-pad or a slab of ornamental crystal! Let us give art a miss; I get as much from passing slowly in my chair in front of shops where everything on display has a new-laid look. Art, in this country means a state of innocence, the jealous care for reputation, the honest saleswoman; art and display here take the form of paper—crinkled, serrated, pleated, gilded—paper in abundance, white as snow, blue as a glacier. Compared with it and its healthy profusion, the linen of our poor France in her time of penury, eked out to the extent of using one corner of a towel after another, will be found slightly abhorrent.

Bananas, late-season but still juicy apples, early strawberries, oranges, eggs, cream whipped or plain! Against that, no cheese—other than by the gramme—no rice, no

butter, except by trickery or arrangement. "What, no
gruyère in Switzerland? You can't mean it!" We simply
burst out laughing. We took it for a joke at our expense
as newcomers, until the staid solemnity of the local inhabitants changed the look on our faces: "No, we have
none for the moment," said the charming young lady, a
native of Geneva. She wore well cut clothes and jewellery;
but she could not procure either butter or cheese. Brought
up to respect restrictions, it never entered her head to
get round them. Perhaps the devil does not exist in
Switzerland!

And gorged with other good things we would console
ourselves with bread alone, *pain-gâteau, pain-brioche,
pain-gourmandise.* So good was it that we feared giving
full rein to our appetite and dared not, at table, ask for a
second helping more than twice.

I have advanced only by small relays, if I dare so to
express myself, in getting to know what amenities Geneva
has to offer. Spring was hesitant, and from a bed of suffering one does not take any but a restricted view of the
lives of the hale and hearty. My strength was at a low ebb
by eight in the evening, when the tray would arrive set
with raw salads, grilled meat, green vegetables and fruit
—don't we all know by heart the list of a prescribed
menu!—and after that came my illuminated entertain-
ment. Through the open window, framing a blue that
subtly deepens with the shades of night, I can see a stretch
of the lake which reflects a bridge and quaysides, and
till past midnight its confines are delineated by multicoloured electric lamps, street lamps, and strings of

fairy lights. Tomorrow the early morning haze will restore to my view the iridescent cathedral, seeming almost to quiver as it is hoisted above the rooftops with its strange glazed domes that brood over its inner sanctuaries. Tomorrow I shall have the peace of a misty sunrise and the curvetting swallows. In the evening, the banners of multicoloured light dip in the lake and ripple over the surface. One particular " advertisement blue " glorifies the national clock-and-watch trade and where this azure strikes across an absinthe-green its colour is enhanced, while a deep crimson spreads out as far as the prow-like breasts of three swans poised above their own reflection.

Certainly it is a pleasure to lie facing a spectacle of lights and shades without so much as having to raise oneself on an elbow, without craning one's neck or sitting up in bed, and never to take one's eyes off it till the curtain of their lids is lowered. Whatever is easily come by is always a pleasure, even when distilled by a drop of bitterness : if I did not suffer—here and here, and again here—this . . . well, this agony, I should never have thought of positioning my bed, calculated to a nicety, in the corner where its occupant is afforded an untrammelled view of three horizons. Those who are fit and agile have no need of such convenience.

"I shall go off by myself on a shopping expedition," said a woman friend who was staying a few days in Geneva, "to buy you whatever you think might tempt you here. Let me have a list."

No sooner said than done. For a long time I had wanted

a pepper-mill, properly made, a mill, as they say in my
quarter of Paris, "that grinds", and not one of those
tuppeny-ha'penny little tooth-wheel objects that wear out
in next to no time and can be found in any of our multiple
stores at home. I also wanted a braid of thread and a braid
of silk made up in the old-fashioned way in needlefuls of
equal length and various colours, tied tight at either end
like saveloys. I now possess them. A little too skimpy,
but a pretty piece of hand-plaiting, of real *passementerie*.
I wanted, too, some four-holed mother-of-pearl buttons for
my underclothes. Mother-of-pearl, and I refused to go back
on my word. Yes, mother-of-pearl, and may the walls
come tumbling down about me! And needles, into the
bargain, some "English" needles (when I was a child
their glazed envelopes were already printed in German),
needles which we, the mistress-craftswomen in hand-
sewing, called "taper-eyed". And some darning wool,
wound on cards. And elastic, to run up the waistbands
for stockinette knickers. And some old-fashioned reels of
cotton, waxed, for stitching leather. Have I ever stitched,
do I stitch, shall I stitch leather? That's beside the point.
And a twist of real silk for repairing the frayed button-
holes on men's clothes. . . . Is there, then, some strange
happiness to be derived from the sight and touch of
certain "requisites" which have never been drastically
changed or modified by any aesthetic concern or shift of
fashion? There is. But since I am still fairly well-off, I
do not put them to their proper use. Entranced by the
magic of contemplative evocation, I deck myself out in
the fine feathers of haberdashery. All the same you would
never have imagined that this right hand of mine, now
rather bunched up from the habit of writing, was once

endowed with the cunning to beget that show-piece of symmetry, sober relievo, solidity: the buttonhole on a male garment! I mean, of course, the buttonhole-stitched buttonhole. There is no poetry in the other, the so-called piped buttonhole.

Hunting for needles for crewel-work is labour in vain. France is a void, Switzerland a barren desert. For ages past the answer given me in the big shops all over France has been: "We don't stock such things. Of course, I'm not saying that in the past . . ." with the head on one side, you know, rather like a dog when offered an empty bowl, and as a consolation prize I am offered darning-needles! I plan, when my dearest friend takes to driving me out again and has recovered his patience, to stop at all the little village haberdashers, the proper kind, with a glass panelled door and tinkling bell, where buttons are to be found in the wool basket, wool in the boot-lace drawer, bootlaces in the zip-fastener container, where a strong smell of pickled herring is all pervasive, and where, finally, a small girl turns toward the murky back of the shop with a plaintive "Mum, I can't find anywhere the sort of needles the lady is asking for!"

Six weeks. Ought I to exclaim "Already!" or "Only six!"? The days pass, all alike, intent on running their course, each scarred at the beginning, middle, and end by physical pain, that sharp recall to life. Dear-Doctor-till-tomorrow still has his gentle voice and his big heart that takes up too much room in his big breast and makes him wheezy. The weather is fine—no, it's going to be fine. Covered by cloud, a white sun is melting the snows on the flanks of the Jura. The return of winter, which has so disheartened Paris, is welcomed by Geneva with opulent serenity. In this hotel the boilers have been rekindled and, in addition to the central heating, parabolical radiators have been installed in every corner, in much the same way that amateur gardeners can't see a gap in their rockery without popping in a fern frond or saxifrage.

Yet no feigned apostasy on the part of hoary winter can outwit or discourage the Judas trees, the double cherries, the lilacs of every hue, by this time obstinately set on their forward course. The start once made, they will sleep out of doors and bloom. Another denial of winter rises at dusk, from the peacefully dormant and rarely sluiced mud at the bottom of the lake. Throughout my wheel-chair perambulations I have to hold my nose against its floating sickly-sweet fragrances. Not enough salt in it. Your true-born Genevan, on the other hand, will sigh in ecstasy "Oh, that smell from the lake! It brings tears to my eyes, each time it comes back to me after I've been away." The green vein of the Rhône, flowing in at great depth, refuses to mingle with the common eddies, and cleaves its forceful path through the waters of Lac Léman, to escape, stabbed by the golden darts of the sun at its zenith.

The sparrow, that perky pedestrian! I had not intended to speak of it. I wished simply to give it food, and leave things at that. But in Geneva the town sparrow takes the initiative and can teach me a thing or two, whether I like it or not. Generations of worthy citizens have gone to the making of generations of trustful birds.

The French bookseller, only three steps away—five or six turns of the wheel to my mode of approach—has been quick to pick up the customs of the country. "When winter comes, we divide the birds between us," he told me, "not for the purpose of eating them, but to look after them. On a night of sudden sharp frost a few winters ago, I had to get out of bed to go and free a gull which had its legs trapped by the ice at the edge of the lake, right in front of my door, the poor thing!" I too am in his debt, for he brings my fare of second-hand books out on to the pavement when I am unable to put foot to the ground, and in a stage whisper promises me "a Peter Cheyney" for the following week. He knows that for all the long days of spring the nights are not so short as the sparrows make out.

I can put up with their chirping as well here as in the Palais-Royal, for its modulation is so limited that it does not always break into my dearly acquired morning sleep. But I did not foresee that at the hour when the immaculate waiter brings in my tray and pulls aside the curtains drawn across my open window, no, I had not foreseen that at that hour my eyes would light upon not the *entry* of the sparrows into my room, but their exit. Seven of them, the colour of mice, came out from under my bed and went to rejoin their cheeping friends on the little balcony.

From that day on, I had difficulty in following the course of their familiarity, their demands upon me, I should rather say. Their appetite is unrelenting rather than insatiable. Three female birds started a nursery on my balcony for their young who had already sprouted feathers but still gave a pretty good imitation of the shrill insistence and shiverings of famished fledglings.

Jeanne Loewer brought me, from the Chaux-de-Fonds, a large round loaf of stale bread for the early morning regimental breakfast. The minute spindle-shaped females held their own against the round-breasted and better feathered cocks, their cheeks and wing plumage coquettishly marked. From watching them I have come to learn a little about that stranger, the bird, telling myself that, given four legs, it would look far more arresting than it does with its two wings crossed over its back, like Napoleon.

The mock-mahogany moulding at the foot of my bed later served as a perch for these lickspittle beggars who outstared me, bombarded me with their sharp, impatient calls and caught bread-crumbs thrown to them as would a French bull-dog. No sooner had I shut myself in the bathroom than they protested in increasing numbers that I should open the door again. The culmination came during siesta-time one warm and fleecy afternoon, when I became aware of some unusual movement close beside me, yet one that touched my heart. I found a pair of them, one close against the other, in a fold of the bed-spread. In an access of bliss, my effort to lean over them must have made too sudden a stir, for away they flew. This gave me fair warning that the time was not far off when I should discover one individual among their small, indefinite band, the particular one, the one who preferred me and was mine by preference. With the animal world, we are subject to the same perils every time. To choose, to be chosen, to love: the very next moment we are beset by anxiety, the danger of loss, and the fear of spreading regret. What an array of big words when the subject

is but a sparrow! Yes, a sparrow. In love, there is never a
question of smallness.

.

In the closing days of April, prior to the cold snap,
"the darling buds of May" and the kerria were setting
an example in their whites and yellows to the roses of
summer, and the first gentians, down from their mountain fastnesses to the florists, were refreshing themselves
in my tooth-glass, their stalks on a pad of damp moss,
which helps the flowers to drink. Their sole beauty lies
in their uncompromising azure blue; there must be some
reason why we find ourselves so sensibly affected by blue!
Age-old evocations of the firmament, a moist mirage in
desert eyes, all that we hold to be eternal, is readily blue.
The corolla of a gentian is tight-stretched on umbrella-
ribs, the cordate cyclamen leaf is lined with mauve india-
rubber: the edelweiss is pure cotton-wool. None of the
three thereby loses its seductive charms and emblematic
character of innocence. I am not forgetting that
ubiquitous intruder, the narcissus! It is everywhere. Year
after year it draws its devotees to Les Avants, where
celebrations are held in its honour. And how do they
honour the narcissus? By killing it. It is sacrificed by the
million. Let us shed no tears, that's all it is good for.
Once picked it is tied up in bunches that quickly wilt
unless plunged into water. Its journey down from Les
Avants by car, van or cycle, has steeped the road in
unchecked, horizontally spreading scent, in the toils of
which we first exclaimed "How divine!" then later
"How nauseating!" Surely there can be few who are
put off the lilac by its sovereign if funerary scent, the lilac

in any of its varieties, blue, purple or mauve, or the sparse and delicate thyrsus of the Rouen lilac! My mother "Sido" used to say of this *varin* variety "I can never make up my mind whether its scent is rather nice or perfectly horrid! "

In many a plot the cherry trees here have overtopped the walls or spread beyond the party hedges. Green yesterday, the fruit is ruddy today, and tomorrow will be ruddier, rounder, heavier still. It acquires an even coating of red, almost glazed, and then it is tempting to eye, mouth and hand. Stretch out an arm, and it is mine, yours, ours for the picking. I pass the trees every day, and I notice that never a cherry is missing. In my part of France, a good shaking was just as likely to drop an urchin hidden in the branches as a good shower of cherries. "You cannot tempt the Devil," the pilferer might plead in self defence, cherries in his mouth and cherries in his pockets. In Switzerland, as I have told you, they have no devil.

III

I HAVE received a love letter: *"Madame Colette, I adore you! I am a very handsome fellow. If you will not say me nay, I shall pay you a call and give you a kiss on the nose."* It was signed "Béni". I did not care to throw away my last chance of having an affectionate interview with a Prince-at-the-very-least-oriental.

He came, attended by a female slave who called herself his mistress. He evinced no disdain when treading the worn carpet of my hotel bedroom, and to start with my dearest friend and I did not know what to say to him; but he was not put out by our lack of words, nor did this deprive him of his princely expression of friendliness.

He was rose-pink—as indeed those Persians known as "Cream" should be when without blemish and, as was this gentleman, loaded with honours, medals and First Prizes. He was almost copper pink, his front paws not a far remove from the good earth, but rising in tone towards the tail. Clad like a fairy, he seemed miraculously at ease in the midst of a cloud of fur that beat against his sides at every step, and provided him at the back with breeches of insubstantial fluff. His coat was a profusion of clustered curls on chest and belly, and escaped from either ear in feathery tufts.

I hesitate to speak of his eyes, not knowing how to

24

capture their exact shape, the wide gleam in them of
liquid gold and amber, the calm confidence with which
they returned our gaze, and their latent smile, the outcome of a petted childhood. Round his nostrils too was
the bloom of the same rare shade of copper pink.

To increase our speechless adoration, he spoke. The
voice of the Angora is ordinarily soft and low, without
prejudicing their amative periods when they are changed
into howling demons. He jumped on to my quaking knees
and, since he had promised it, gave me a kiss on the nose.
He was pleased to display symptoms of curiosity about
my bathroom and over the cheeky sparrows on the
balcony, to whom he delivered a pithy address in the
tremulous tones that inform the feathered race of the
exact sentiments of a cat towards them. Wanting for
nothing, he was without covetous desires, and when we
saw him turn away from the birds to go in chase of
a ball of crumpled paper, we uttered cries of delighted
affection.

I held him for a moment in a tight embrace, tufted and
sweet-smelling as a bunch of flowers. He gave me another
kiss or two, on the tip of my nose and under my ear, and
all the while his slave was expatiating on his noble line-
age and the fruits of victory he brought back from every
competition. She added a few relevant details: " He is
unmatched for cleanliness; he not only puts up with but
actually insists on his daily toilet with brush and comb;
if at times it is his pleasure to show signs of abject sub-
mission, the slightest reprimand will cut him to the quick
and may even ruin his appetite." I took solemn note of
these "light touches" that added authenticity to his portrait; I transcribe them here in a suitably genteel tone.

Anything to do with cats, in my thoughts or in my writing, must never be treated with banter.

The musical ear of a cat clearly differentiates between familiarity and affection. It was not merely from her delight in playful fantasy that the Last Cat enjoyed my "Cat, come here at once! Cat, go to bed!" that formed part of the evening ritual. Gaily she scampered away, racing to her basket, and giving a passable imitation of a dog obeying orders. But it is true that the cat prefers the intonations of the human voice which come nearest to singing. In my few remarks to "Béni", I observed the essential protocol. All the more since, to his other perfections, was added that childlike air of majesty which Angoras are slow to discard. Far removed from his character were the depth and intensity of the Last Cat, with her too ready aptitude to feel and express grief. For instance the year when, rather against her better nature and following a brief encounter with the shoeblack on the corner, the black and white bistro cat, and the grocer's small ginger, she produced a fine bastard daughter, striped, smiling, and half-witted, that we called Jantille. At once the Cat drove her from sight and affection out of pure jealousy, so much so that the very name of Jantille on the lips of either one of us would evoke from her a feeble little anguished cry. So we gave Jantille away as a present to the Curé of Mesnuls, and the Cat's aggrieved heart found peace.

It is to "Béni" that I owe this retrospective daydream. His resplendent presence, memories of the Last Cat, whatever acts as a touchstone to renew or remind me of cat personalities or cat characters, at once takes me back to a past climate that used to be both poignant and essential, but has since been renounced by me, prudently and with detachment.

Béni, for his part, seemed desirous of going to sleep on my knees, over which was draped my soft vicuna rug. He had already settled down to a rippling purr when his mood changed and, starting to mew in a minor key, he led his slave towards the door. The princely visit was ending with the end of his patience, the short-lived, brittle patience of the feline species that suddenly snaps and makes as putty in a man's hands the trained lion, the broken-spirited tiger in its cage, and the puma sulking in tears!

Amiable still, though distant, Béni made short shrift of farewell courtesies. He even rebuffed me with his soft cat's paw, conditioned by custom to gentleness yet ready to remind me that, dormant in their sheath—indubitably pink—it held sharp-pointed claws.

On my outings I drive along at the leisurely pace of a lady of the Second Empire. A pony-chaise could overtake me. There is always so much to look at when one travels slowly. Contrasting beauties effaced by speed fall into their proper perspective. My years and infirmities have surely earned me the right to go slow, to stop at whim beside a narcissus, a purple orchis, or a wild strawberry! No need now for my dearest friend, while at the wheel, his chin jutting out like a radiator cap, to interfere with his "No, no! No wild lavender, no honeysuckle, no cytisus! No time for a snack before Saulieu! You'll make havoc of all my timetables!" Nowadays it is he who picks my wild hyacinths for me. In the long run there is something to be said for having arthritis.

Thus my stoppings and startings become voyages of discovery; I go from garden-restaurant to riverside garden, I take stock of bowers and arbours and rose gardens. Here the municipal gardeners are busy planting out the roses they have kept hidden off-stage by the thousand. Roses assume a military elegance when paraded in serried ranks. As we pass them by, certain precocious battalions salute us with the special scent of their species, the unmistakable breath of "tea" and "tea hybrids". How quickly they go—how quickly am I going! Yet an aged body like mine clings fast to the winter of its discontent and its attendant ills, wraps itself up in shawls and rugs, derives a secret satisfaction from the chilly aftermath of the doctor's visit, profits from the anticipated loss of strength to withdraw into itself, and forget the spring. It is not possible to deny the spring. On a clear day the lake, though niggardly with indigo, might well be the Mediterranean. Children spangle the town with their little check dresses; grown-up girls go about bare-legged. Luxury is manifest in the spotless garment, the constant laundering, the fluffy jumpers that are the envy of Paris. And what a fine display of heads of hair, with never any need for the horrible "hair-pad"! Resplendent but not too feminine angels boldly fend their way through the peak-hour crowds, their hair a torch, their bare knees like glazed, crackling fruit skins.

I admire, I rejoice, I get about, I come into contact with all these long-legged Atalantas whose praises I sing— oh no, a thousand times no, don't run away with the idea that I am jealous, or sad! Do me the honour of believing

that I do know how to make the most of what is left me
of my part, do know how to bear lightly what would have
seemed heavy in days gone by, and derive from the flaw
by which metaphorically I am ploughed and furrowed a
certain . . . yes, I shall say it . . . a certain nobleness of
spirit. I hesitate before putting down such an expression,
sounding it out, taking its measure: what if it be too
grand for me! Believe, at any rate, that I have no need
for all the consideration I receive, that I laugh inwardly
when the kind-hearted, on my behalf, go as far as to use
the word "asceticism", as though it were a fitting rank
or title. Does anyone suppose that it would be easy to
escape the clutches of asceticism!

Will the various remedies which the Good-bye-till-
tomorrow-Doctor inflicts on me one day become a source
of amusement? One of them is greasy and glacial. Another
is more penetrating, has more quills than a sea-urchin.
There is yet another, which the body, stunned at receiving
so many steel-pointed light rays, cannot help but question.

Here I am, with two months all but gone, longing to
drink a toast to what the future holds in store for me of
the unpromised and unknown. Dear-Doctor-till-tomorrow, I suffer from hope, and from modesty, and I ask you
as few questions as I can. After the time of roses in their
ordered ranks comes, I know, the symmetrical blaze of
geraniums, of scarlet salvias, and then will come the
dahlias, and later the chrysanthemums. Let us look no
further. While resting on shores made to bloom under
civic control, I have entered again into close friendship
with all the wild flowers of the Swiss meadows, which
are brought in to the proprietress of this hotel swathed
in a tangle of nondescript greenery. They come into my

room only after they have been sorted out, picked over and tastefully arranged by her own hands. Here the funny little face of some labiate nibbles at the wing of a bee-orchis—the fringed carmine beards of the ragged-robin emerge from a blue foundation of self-heal—the golden buttons of ranunculus from meadow and stream are wreathed in the insubstantial mist of their umbels—the three "Pasque flowers", mauve, violet and white, form the gauzy edging of a large, shallow bowl filled with lilies of the valley, the last of the season—already, a suspicion of baldness silvers the crimson clover. The crimson clover already! Have I then sacrificed, aided and abetted by my dearest friend, almost the quarter of one year to ministrations of which I cannot yet compute the range or the rewards, let alone alleviation? Not a soul has mentioned a possible cure to me, yet a constant appeal is made to my moral resources. Splendid! Least said soonest mended! In any case, there are so many methods of cure —perhaps I may invent one myself. To a dash of daring add a moderate dose of arbitrariness, a liberal dose of astonishment, much after the fashion of that ingenious child who stretched a piece of stuff over two rods set crosswise at the end of a stick and shouted "Maman, do look, I've just invented the umbrella!"

ᔕᕼ IV *Paris*

THIS year, next year, some time, never! When shall we acquire what we most want, some of us poor folk who are almost at the end of our tether, pent within the four walls of a room, wedged between desk and book-case, assailed by the footfall on the floor above and the clatter of wooden soles on the staircase without? Not tomorrow, not this year, will Paris provide us with one or two " Gardens for Adults ". That the most pressing need takes precedence, that first there must be " Gardens for Children ", I do not dispute. And where can a large enough site be found? I am not to be taken in by small talk of that nature: when Paris requires a vacant site, she finds one. Not without first looking for it, I agree. After which they might very well endow a site for V.I.P.s. The garden of the Palais-Royal is the very thing for such persons. It holds few attractions for children, who have done it infinite hurt by their presence and their games. Sand and gravel are non-existant, the earth has been stamped into insensibility, and it is forbidden to water the soil— the lawns and flowerbeds alone are entitled to have their thirst quenched, and the gardener tends these lovingly— what we call our " Court " has to rest content solely with the slow and time-honoured impregnations from showers

31

of rain, urine of dogs, and human excrement—let me put
"children's droppings", to make it sound better.

Here all is an open stage, where the principal players
are the children. Many are charming, most are gifted
with remarkable agility. The thin-bodied outstrip the
more robust. Their skill in throwing and catching a ball
holds my attention as keenly as a sporting event. At my
window yesterday, a Sunday, I was fascinated by a baby
girl of four or so, squat for her age, who was disporting
herself in the sabbatical silence with two male members
of her family, her father and uncle no doubt. This child
so intent on her outdoor sport repaid all the attention I
bestowed on her, so deft was she at stopping the ball with
her foot, at throwing it back straight—and with either
hand—so adept at falling bare-legged and bare-armed on
the hard ground without a word of complaint. But, as I
could well see, she was an exception, as are child prodigies
on the stage or in the circus, so much so that when told to
do so she sat down in the wind and the sun and stayed
still like an athlete. And like an athlete she had put on
flesh: her face was a good colour, but far from improved
by two strands of plaited hair scragged back over each
ear and tied with a tag of ribbon. An exception, but a
welcome exception, formed by discipline and self-confidence. It would have been beyond the comprehension,
and envy, of most of our Palais-Royal children, that a
small girl of four, from some sense of quasi-professional
pride, could be capable of behaving with such zest and
restraint.

Not all the scenes beneath my window are as pleasant
to watch as that. Into my magnificent quadrangle seethe
a hotch-potch of young people all full of beans who, since

the war, intolerable and intolerant, have cast off the
shackles of restraint and guidance. Quick on their feet
but not fleet-footed, for their steps are conditioned by the
imperfections of shoes no longer made to fit, they hop-
and-go-one as sylphs might hobble if shod. Smitten from
early youth with a passion for every sort of competitive
game, like born neuropaths they follow their bent with
uninhibited disregard for convention: they are true children of Paris.

In our royal enclosure we have never enjoyed any
greater hygienic comfort and convenience than Versailles
could boast under Le Grand Roi. Apart from the plush
and luxury of the Restaurant Véfour and the amenities
of the neighbouring theatre, there is not a single *buen-
retiro* in sight. La Civette, to the greater glory of My Lady
Nicotine, has pulled down its time-honoured mahogany
stalls, which venerable dames used to tend with such care.
Of what matter is that to the Garden's imperious guests,
the children? When the need comes upon them, down
slip the little shorts and up go the little skirts and . . .
There are even simpler methods still. The infant in arms
will pipe up from its pram with a cry of alarm; without
rising from her wrought-iron chair, that indestructible
relic of past ages, the mother or watcher will snatch it up
and hold it at arms' length, as though it were a strainer
of liquids and solids! Yesterday, immediately below my
window, nine little puddle-stains all along the stone flags
testified to the fact that among the chairs that afternoon
nine children had slept, taken food, and . . . evacuated
Oh, what malodorous incense rises in the evening air!

The war and its aftermath conditioned our children to
jungle practices. A few days ago I saw two bigger boys

of about twelve coming my way. They stopped at the
first tree on the Valois side of the pleached alley. I thought
to myself 'They're going to micturate in unison '—we're
quite accustomed to that—'against one of those old decaying trees that never quite die.' Not at all. Lowering their
already man's-size trousers, they jointly deposited the
copious insignia of their brief visit. Throughout the operation they chatted amicably, without bravado and without
shame. Shame and shamelessness mean nothing to them.
But since it was broad daylight the passers-by, for their
part, did look the other way.

With a child, making a nuisance of itself is instinctive
and terrifyingly ingenious. The appetite for destruction—
in other words, invention—has to be satisfied when and
where it can. The return of spring sees the pink chestnut
candelabra cut to shreds by the stone-throwers, and brings
back the stalkers-on-the-slates so skilled in dislodging at
one fell blow the nests full of young birds from under
the ceilings of the arcade.

A generation of disheartened parents confront the
children of today. It would be easy for me to fill these
pages with shameful tales of child hucksters, schoolboy
gangsters, striplings who act as stooges for big-time
criminals: in short, of children who have never known
the joys of childhood. Will they, perhaps—in the words
of Labiche—come to know childhood in old age?

But I haven't the heart to curse them, my lively sparrows intoxicated by their own chirrupings, my whistling
little cobras, my embryo artillerymen, corn-crake-voiced
chatterboxes and maniac trumpeters, all the more because
I have never lost either the memory or the benefits of a
parental upbringing which instructed me in silence before

all else. I cannot spend my time abusing them, because I observe them and by observation make them my own. I do not lay claim to them in the name of a pseudo-maternity which has never come easily to me, but from my window above I recognise in them my own blood, my own race, my own past, my own faults, whether reclaimed by time or aggravated by age. Ideal greed that feeds on fancy! This naughty child secretly belongs to me, as the animal with whom I exchange some sign of recognition is mine, as one of the plants in the flower-bed is mine since I am perhaps the only one to know its name: *penstemon*. When I passed on this name to another citizeness of the Palais-Royal I received in exchange a brief shrug and for answer " Don't make me laugh! How can I believe a name like that! " I was in half a mind to take her up: " You don't want it? Then give it me back. I shall share it only with M. Henri, the gardener, who loves his flower-beds." And having classified it among the objects of my ideal possessions, along with my fillies, my newly hatched chicks, all the marvellous offspring of my own modest phantasmagoria, I shall put the *penstemon* to much the same use as did Théophile Gautier the flower of his imagination, the *angsoka*.

WHAT a fierce, unparalleled, interminable summer
this has been, rising again and again from its ashes,
converting Normandy into a parched Ardèche, Burgundy
into a waste of esparto-grass, laying bare and dry the beds
of all the mountain torrents, as well as the bottom mud of
ponds where frogs expired and fish lay gasping! Only
now, when the time has come round for the nights to turn
cold, can a good word be put in for the fearful summer,
responsible as it was for so many of our food shortages.
In no sense to restore it to grace and favour, for it is
past redemption. Its savagery began at dawn, with the
animals athirst and all the herbivores deprived of sus-
tenance. You might see a man using only one small
watering-can to sprinkle a cabbage field, one of those
huge fields that in good years do honour to the outskirts
of a town, a single man among ten thousand yellowing
cabbages. You might see a cow that, while pulling up the
stubble blade by blade, had swallowed ten kilos of earth
and died of it. You might see . . .

No, I shall never be able to link together a series of
agreeable memories with the aid of such pictures. They
blacken and reduce to cinders my favourite pastime of
day-dreaming for pleasure. Forty-one degrees centigrade
in Rue de Beaujolais at noon, and thirty-seven at two

o'clock in the morning: how far away it all seems now when, through my high half-open windows, the December air forces a vertical passage, whitened by fine frozen snow which, for a brief moment, wreathes with a halo my blue lantern that burns by night and by day. A few seconds are sufficient for the cold to take possession of my room. Quick! Now's the moment—without making a physical movement of any kind—to plunge back into whatever of the summer's bounty was least harsh and dehydrated, there to discover something to make the mouth water, to bring colour to hand and dress, something pertaining to freshets and dew: let us return to the brief recompense, all the more real in that it was unsolicited, granted me at the fiercest moment of the ferocious summer: vintage time on the slopes of Brouilly.

Most certainly, for an arthritic like myself, the worst is not the getting about from place to place, always provided that the journey is made by car. The worst is taking ten steps across the room, walking five yards along the garden, having my night's rest broken by sudden, sharp jabbing thrusts of pain, reaching out with the quick, impulsive gesture of youth in an attempt to pick up my stick or lift down a book—oh, how inveterate is youth, its agility now purely of the mind, and chastised the moment it strains at the leash! As for the stairs, their descent is now a matter of humiliation and guile: for when a stranger passes, do I not stop and, standing still, pretend to be putting on a glove or fumbling in my bag! Once the stranger is safely out of the way, I laugh at myself and my old woman's wiles.

But put me into a car, with a cushion here and a cushion there, and away we go! You won't hear another word from me for a prolonged stretch of miles. In bygone days it was the Cat who decided, by a yawn of hunger or some discomfort of the bladder, the spot where our Ark should come to rest. She ate little on a journey, and feared travel sickness. A nip at Saulieu, a lap at Vienne, with a refresher of grass between times. My requirements are on a less modest scale than hers. When she was of the company, we hardly had time to finish our woodland picnic before she demanded to be back in " her " car to smooth every hair of her coat, blue as a storm cloud coming up from the west.

As I was saying—saying to myself, rather, though I was committing it to paper—it was a masterful decision on the part of my dearest friend that got me away, as he alone knew how, at crack of dawn on a morning that reeked of heatwave, melting asphalt and dried-up river beds, set on a course for the slopes that border the Rhône. There the small tight-bunched grapes are less decorative than the opulent Provençal muscat, that trails its six-pound allurements under the vine-stock and offers its fresh-skinned belly to the lizard.

What benefits could I hope to reap from the Beaujolais vintage? The never varying torrid heat, my very helplessness, everything seemed fated to keep me apart from such a rough and rustic festival. I would have been content to listen to the sounds with which it covered the hills, the wains creaking along the rough tracks beside which I took my morning nap. Voices hazy with early morning fatigue arose from the heights of a neighbouring vineyard and then declined, descending ever lower as the sun rose higher. I could picture the slow work of picking, the baskets filled, the increasingly parched throats of any who

thought to slake their thirst by biting into a bunch. I kept
the persistent summer at bay on the far side of closed
Venetian blinds, on the side of the flaming ball of fire,
the flies, the demented wasps, and the dusty mint plants,
the side on which could be viewed a glint of a dazzling
fragment of the Saône as it sparkled in the valley, far
away. I exercised a modicum of patience. I listened to the
red-tailed wall-creepers rustling the ivy above the fountain
and cutting the thread of its jet.

But better things were in store for me. Friendship can
achieve much. A chain of linked arms settled me in the
car one day, and in the recesses of one of his private
chambers, I bearded My Lord Wine, whose threshold I
had thought never to pass.

He received me in the cool bosom of a hill without my
having to put foot to the ground. It was I, seated in my
chariot, who had the air of a conqueror. With its great
door thrown back, his Palace had the appearance of a
sequestered grotto, and from its spacious ceiling he enveloped me at one and the same time in an icy cope of
motionless air, the divine and mushy odour of crushed
grapes, and the droning hum of their fermentation.
Lamps shone like twinkling stars along vaults a hundred
metres in length; vats spumed long thinning festoons of
rosy froth over their sides; a team of dappled horses, blue-
tinted in the half-light, were nonchalantly munching
grapes that had tumbled to the floor; emanations from
the new wine, heavy, impure and but newly born,
blended with the steam rising from the sodden horses.

A sparkle of ruby red flickered over the chased ribs and
bosses of a silver cup which, at the end of an unseen arm,
a man's hand flourished in front of me: " A forty-four

in its prime, Madame. But come back and taste the forty-
seven when the time comes round! It will be more than
the equal of this."

Come back! How probable, how easy this sounded as
I held the cold rim of the brimming cup between my lips,
under the arching grotto that barred ingress to the heat
outside!

As those about me were of the opinion that the *grand
vin*, the starry cavern, and the shade of the hillside tunnel
could perhaps be considered as antidotes, we made
another trip, this time by night, taking another route to
climb another slope. This time the shade was provided
by a wistaria that clung to all four sides of a courtyard;
issuing from a single trunk, like a huge writhing python,
it rose hugely to heights where it became lost in its own
foliage. The covered-in courtyard, lit by arc-lamps, rang
with the clangor of voices, wheels and heavily shod feet,
for the forty or so vintagers of the estate were on their
way down to their repast, bringing in with ᵥhem their
aroma of male vigour and the juices of the vine. How
dearly I should have loved to follow them down! Our
cold collation on the ground floor was a feast of ham
liberally padded with fat, sausages that had a whiff of
new harness, and a special cheese, called "strong", that
provokes an unquenchable thirst.

All honour to labour where honour is due: below stairs,
the forty vintagers were to sit down to the better table,
consisting of omelettes, pork, veal and poultry, washed
down with a wine which, like the finest rubies when held
to the light, keeps the clear brilliance of its generous, full-
blooded colour.

The fatigue that follows a faultless meal, served with

a young vintage wine on a summer night with no dewfall, can be agreeable enough, provided it is not forced or prolonged. In the court-yard at the time of our departure, under the swinging arc-lamps, the huge wistaria coiled its living spirals. But, since we were the first to leave, I could not appreciate any but the sharpest sounds emerging from the great silence that little by little was settling over the hillface: flights of brittle-winged elytrons jarring against the standard lamps at the entrance; the hoof-beats of an unharnessed horse clattering along a cross-road and, above all, soft music on the ear, invisible and held in reverence by all, the never failing babble of the freshet, the last, this fevered year, where gasping hill and parched dale could slake their thirst.

VI

F ARGUE and I, confined to our respective beds, used
to talk on the telephone. Not very often, but at considerable length. I dearly loved, and shall always love,
his fat, rich, infinitely elastic voice, with a shade of suffoca-
tion over it caused by chronic bronchitis. My memory
bears me out that our verbal exchanges were never anything but affectionate, frivolous, riddled with news of our
work or of our leisure, and of course with every kind of
reminiscence.

I was always curious to learn from him the manner
of his suffering and the nature of his physical pain.
"Today it's hammers, yesterday I was in the grip of a
vice, a sort of continual grinding," he would say, and
then go on to question me about my periods of sleep and
sleeplessness, but I knew full well that he was reproaching
me for my failure to sound romantic: whereas in his
mouth an ostentatious choice of words would throw a
glamour over his very disease. . . . I shall make time and
space to talk further of him, as he used to be.

When he allowed me into his house to see his " Family
Portraits all hung on the line," I had good reason to show
my delight and gratitude. Thereafter I wanted to see
more and more of him. I wanted Fargue both in the flesh
and in the mind's eye, Fargue traipsing across Lipp,

42

Fargue strolling down the street with his soft, untiring tread, and above all I wanted to see Fargue. Arrangements were made for my transference one day last summer, I being the lesser sufferer of the two. The first stage by car, through the streets at dusk on a fine evening—the streets of Paris, Fargue's undisputed kingdom, glittering with gold-dust, rich with his insults and charm of manner—a journey at whose end I knew him to be waiting for me.

At the Rue du Montparnesse end they bundled me into the luggage-lift sprinkled with coal. The ascent brought me to Fargue. Some whim or other prompted him to be found seated at table, so that I might think him capable of rising at any given moment, I can only suppose, to offer me his arm and bring me to rest at his table.

Six guests all told; but as how many should I reckon Léon-Paul Fargue, presiding like a Buddha, with all his eloquence and gaiety? He was at his best that evening, to the extent of giving reassurance to Goudeket and myself. I won't swear that he deceived our friends Doctor Martha Lamy and Professor Paulette Gauthier-Villars and even Chériane herself. But he made a good meal, scolded and laughed as scornfully as an intolerant prince. He complained of the too blue blueness of his sheets, and depicted for us what he alone could see. He talked to the cat, affectionately, for the cat was as glossy, as dark and beautiful as Chériane. Facing me was a portrait of her, large and striking, prominent and lifelike as a guest at table. To my right the ledge of the open window cut off the trunks of the plane trees; the lover of the streets had his lodgings among the branches.

I can find nothing to say about this last evening that is either more, or less, deserving of report, of regret, or of being affectionately preserved in the memory of his friends. No single one of us, not even Fargue himself, rose to the occasion. None of us felt either the need or desire to applaud, to make an occasion of it, or to register exceptional surprise. But I know that the six guests have not forgotten a single moment of it, that in the bitter certainty of there being no next time, we, his faithful and unfortunate friends, all feel ourselves to be the poorer.

I have not been to the theatre since I went to see *La Folle de Chaillot*. Not that I have not wanted to go; but, as Pauline says, "it creates too much of a song and dance" to get me comfortably installed in a theatre or cinema. Helplessness breeds timidity. I do not mean to say that it leads one to self-indulgence. Abstinence surely does not ruin the stomach for every kind of relish! In consideration of the length of time that one or two of my senses had been deprived of gratification, I should have expected the more readily available appeal to the ear and the delights and surprises offered to the eye to have given me a rejuvenated enthusiasm. And yet there I sat as wary as when I was a dramatic critic. I had hoped to be more agreeably surprised.

On the first encounter the shock was agreeable enough: the auditorium of the Athénée, encrusted with glittering gilt. Meretricious but magnificent! What a wealth of golden fruit and swags, with as many breasts as apples, as many pears as garlands and thighs! An auditorium for a real theatre, a real auditorium for a theatre, where Bérard's rollicking blues and reds were set off by a long lustreless black figure, the figure of Jouvet standing out against the set, Jouvet with jet sewn into his black tights, a long black exclamation mark!

Last night I committed the downright folly of re-reading *Le Festin de Pierre,* the cause of my considerable embarrassment in listening to the piece. It was like listening to a musical composition with the score open on my knees. All the same I was able to enjoy unreservedly my right to give no opinion. If I were forced to form a judgment on Don Juan as played by an actor who " walks off with ", after a line or two and a couple of capers, a pair of country wenches, I should find it hard to scrap my own conception of Don Juan as sombre, self-willed—I was about to write " abstemious "—endowed with that deep-rooted misogyny which women find so attractive.

This was by no means the first time I had been tempted by Don Juan. I had dealings with him in *Le pur et l'impur,* but not at any great length and only perfunctorily. I had forgotten about Molière and how little he knew about the subject, even less than myself, since it was not enough for him that his hero should have sinned against love. The reason was that treason to love was still beyond the philosophy of his day.

The play moves along, now slap-dash, now strait-laced, dealing harshly with the heretic and driving the seducer to insult religion no less than paternal authority: I should say that we help it on its way by our strained attention— I pride myself on being one of the best audiences I know —embellished as it is with too ingenious dramatic refinements. But how good it was in those surroundings! How they foster unreality! Balconies, mouldings, ceilings, a riot of reds and gold. I had only to lean forward in my stage box to touch the strutting actors with my hand; not one of them was perfect, not one could act badly if he tried. Two or three of them gave me a furtive greeting, a glance of recognition that took them momentarily out of their pretended character.

Outside the Paris rain teemed down in buckets and through it I had to pass to regain my refuge from wind and rain. A strong arm was at hand to give its unfailing support. In the thick of the crowd I knew I should again succumb to the timidity that afflicts cripples, for it is real and obliging pity that they most fear. In the time it took to cross the pavement and enter the car, I should be soaked like all the others, overjoyed like everyone else at having been to the theatre for a Sunday matinée, richer by my store of living images, and busy for the rest of the day with what was not my business but my concern, namely, the art and effort of others, and dearer still—for mistakes are more intelligible than success—the intelligent mistakes of others.

They invaded my room, each an exceptional personality, all three of them so vigorously present and alive, taking up so much space yet never encumbering a room little more than exiguous, the one sitting himself down on the prow of my raft and the other two where best they could.

They came in with their strongly defined characteristics written all over them. Yvonne de Bray, and her warm, well-bred cordiality; Jean Marais, nicknamed Jeannot, with his crest of hair and his irreproachably irregular features; and the young woman who, as recompense for having her face laid bare from ear to tip of nose, from chin to forehead, every line removed from her cheeks and thus rendered glossy as a wet-glazed jar, had suddenly become beautiful enough to play Beauty herself. Heavens! I was forgetting the dog, the dog Moulouk, who owed allegiance to one person only, to Jean Marais. Yet all the time we were together I hardly had cause to remember him; he faded into Jean's shadow, became part of Jean, took the form now of an armchair-leg, now of a small Persian rug, and up to the moment of their departure called no attention to himself, except when earlier in the proceedings he paid a visit to my bathroom on his own initiative.

"What are you looking for? " Jean asked him in an aside.

" A bidet, to drink from," answered the dog.

" To the left," I told him, " behind the bath. The tap's running, and there's always enough water in the pan for you to have a drink."

" Good," said Moulouk, " I'll find it all right, I'm neither deaf nor blind. Plock, plock, plock, plock . . . There's the proof."

Once more he parted the curtains with his wet muzzle and lay down again like a sack of nuts, emitting a sigh, for he could tell from the pitch of our voices that the visit was by no means over and that no one was going to utter the prophetic word. Indeed, our conversation was bright and far-ranging as we touched on this and that; we even rehearsed—at least they did—some scenes from *Chéri*, for a radio programme. For myself, I was perfectly content to watch them, while listening to their voices was an unearned increment. Of the three, Yvonne de Bray's affected me the most nearly. From time to time, when she was made to feel hurt, it would grate on a more enforced

register with the insistence of an engraver intent on his
block. The actress seemed impelled by some sort of
modesty to carry simplicity to excess; she introduced the
tone of a family conversation to one particular scene, and
broke into a sob as into a gale of laughter. Unexpected
inflexions I had not indicated in the text would bring
home her words to an unseeing audience. An actress so
pre-eminently endowed—and one so totally disinterested
—should have it in her to play all rôles.

Turning my attention away from Yvonne, I followed
" Jeannot ", who diminished his huge bulk, his strong
arms, and his strong legs trained to grip the flanks of
film mustangs, to the dimensions required for Chéri.

Jean Marais play Chéri! And why not? In his author's
conception of him, Chéri never had any traits in common
with Musset's wan Lorenzaccio. And for a born actor
what a challenge it is, and a rewarding one at that, to
discover the means so to expand and contract his physique
that a puny man can turn himself into a lusty athlete and
a strapping fellow get inside the shell of a shrimp! The
hardest thing of all for Jean Marais, if he is to play Chéri,
will be to make temporary surrender of his natural innocence. He can at need make himself ugly, as in the part
of the " Beast " (though in that film the grandeur of
despair was hardly ugliness), but where will he go to for
cunning, for soft-spoken insolence and a talent for false-
hood, for the barefaced pleasure of failing, and of recover-
ing only to fail again? For the moment I dreamt, as I
listened to him, of seeing him on the stage. I could well
imagine that it was his innocence, like a nugget of gold,
that choked his big, fierce voice. Time will show. There
is no hurry. For the present my three interpreters, who

were close beside me where I lay in bed, were not playing what I had written, but playing with it. They were gay with the gaiety of beings whose life has one end, one vision, one light, and reckons on a succession of incarnations. They possessed talent enough to throw off time and again the watch on themselves which impedes the inferior artist. "*Nounoune chérie! Nounoune chérie!*", faltered Jean Marais. Nobody had asked of him a stage performance for the radio, yet he collapsed into the arms of Yvonne de Bray, who all at once found strength enough to support and cradle the weight of an athlete. "*Mon méchant—Ma beauté—Te voilà——*". Jeannot made himself hoarse with sobbing, as required; the dazzling blue eyes of Yvonne de Bray, as they gazed at him, were moist with tears. Was all that for me, the solitary spectator? I was under no illusion; it was all for themselves, and, in their own despite, for honour's sake.

Of course I have one, like you, like the rest of the world; but if I never let on, nobody would ever know about it, so discreet am I in my use of it. At this moment it is softly murmuring to me one of Violetta's great arias, the heroine of *La Traviata*.

That full credit may go to the soprano, the accompaniment is a mere poum, poum, poum—poum, poum, poum, in three-time. The *diva* takes advantage of this to do full justice to her soprano voice, but she is not too much for me; for I have moderated the tone, and the sound of my tiny American machine, of an apparent capacity of about a cubic decimetre, does not penetrate beyond the closed door of my room.

What must be must be. After going all through my cupboard of gramophone records, and finding it full to overflowing, I gave them away, and kept only " The Cat's Aria ", an American number which really did make my unforgettable Cat smile. Later on, when a bad illness took the Cat from me, I smashed the record, preferring silence, preferring above all the talent of those compassionately rich and generous people who would sit down at our "cottage" piano: Poulenc, with " Jean Hou-Hou " and *Les Animaux modèles*, Jean-Michel Damase, with his flexible voice, in our *Rouge-gorge* and our *Perle égarée*.

After that we sold the piano to buy a book-case! One memorable day my dearest friend brought home the smallest—but is there not always a smaller than the smallest?—American radio set (no aerial required), which sang all the way up my staircase. We deposited it on my divan-bad, where it started to give a spirited rendering of *L'Enfant et les Sortilèges*: " All you have left me is a single golden hair, like a moonbeam on my shoulder ". Ever since then, it and I have been boon companions. I tone down the great voice inside the body of a dwarf, I employ its ventriloquial gifts as much on Trénet as on Beethoven, and I do not overlook its great virtues on account of its small failings.

I am too antediluvian ever to lose entirely my earliest memory and sense of the miraculous when in the presence of a radio set. How splendid that children the world over can be on terms of intimacy with this polyphonic prodigy! In whatever outdated year was it that I visited, at the invitation of General Ferrier, a hall dominated from floor to ceiling by a vast frame—hexagonal, as far as I can remember—seemingly held together by strands of green silk? If I am not mistaken, the contraption swerved round vertically on one of its sides, giving out a confusion of sounds; these were explained by General Ferrier as coming from various points of origin, for he was a great expert in this rapidly evolving invention which was already one of the world's new wonders.

From within the six sides of this harp and from behind the long strands of green silk, there suddenly came to us the song, far away and limpid, for which one bird alone could be responsible. But someone said "That's Constantinople". Not a soul dared show surprise at this intelligence, for such was the immediacy of our new emotion that a nightingale heard in Paris could not but be oriental, by the same token that a flying carpet is oriental, that the moon is crescent as it rides on high above the silvery Bosphorous.

VII

"*T*HIS *village where we live, set about with woods and a dark fir plantation, is where I teach the village children of twelve and thirteen, telling them of your mother, Madame, and how she would taste before dawn the forbidden fruits of her household chores.* I teach them to know, which is to say to love. If ever, in the course of your existence, no bonds of vassalage have bound you to any overlord . . ."*

There I stop, before I quote the whole letter, and because it concerns only myself, the writer and his office to the young. Surely this one passage is sufficient to give more than an inkling that its author is adept at turning a phrase! How delightfully we obscure denizens of the French countryside can express ourselves when we have a mind to it! I say "we" by reason of the pride I feel in belonging, as regards both native land and love of style in writing, to the same race as my unknown correspondent. He, as he tells us, is a village schoolmaster. Lucky village! Above all, lucky children, who can with confidence entrust themselves to such a guide! I hesitate to write "lucky teacher", unless he is enabled to rise above the rigours of his profession by some especial saintliness that exalts his loneliness and pride. This man has written to me in his native tongue whose crystal purity

---

* See *My Mother's House*, pp. 129-30. English ed. Secker & Warburg.

he exemplifies, being himself passionately devoted to reading, and a contemplatist; he has written to me and shows surprise that I have sent him an answer. The children in his school have also written to me. Using coloured pencils, one has drawn a flower, another a house, and a third, having also drawn a dwelling, tells me " what cannot be seen " on the other side of it. But I have no difficulty in realising what he himself sees there—the garden, two fir trees, and a lawn. When one is twelve, it is easy to see through walls.

The worthy schoolmaster is not my only correspondent. I also receive letters from schoolmistresses, some of whom love to write for the sake of writing, others with a genius for inventing games and other ingenious ploys, who are clever in winning from an unresponsive child the word or smile indicative of so many pledges, so many conquests. Then, in the hour of their success, to whom are they going to relate it? To me. You can well believe, for one day at least, I am filled with pride.

Madame Wattine has sent me a parcel of cornel berries. The good old French name for them is *macres*, or water-caltrops. But cornel sounds more horny, and has the tang of her rural Poix. Water caltrops are so little known, so unappreciated, and last so short a time, being con-sidered a delicacy only in districts where there are ponds, that I should like to say something about them. My appetite for them is as strong as ever. To prise them open I had to make use of one of the stone stairs in the house where I was born. For this strange water fruit, of ooze and autumn bred, forms with its four protective horns when fully ripe a shell of very hard texture, definitely "Chinese" in shape according to Fix-Masseau, and the method prescribed, first to avoid cutting oneself and second to lose nothing of its mealy kernel, is one scoop with a practised hand, a good stout knife, and the step of a stone staircase. In return for which you will acquire blue-black stains, a couple of damaged fingers, and an attack of marsh fever into the bargain if, as I used to do and am still capable of doing, you eat some four hundred caltrops straight off the reel.

"And . . . are they really good?" I am asked by friends deep-dyed with incredulity and circumspection.

I thereupon assume a dreamy, sentimental, and slightly stupid look, in fact become very like the little girl I used to be, and answer "I don't rightly know, but I happen to love them."

Indeed, I know nothing to compare with the taste of these water chestnuts,

> *Prickly, tickling chestnuts,*
> *Which tickle the thighs,*
> *And prick in the pocket,*

as the solitary caltrop-vendor, sack slung over shoulder, used to cry up and down the streets of Saint-Sauveur. At four sous a hundred, and he gave good measure!

The caltrop, or water chestnut, has a bluish white flesh the consistency of a wax candle and a kernel which, like its husk, is neither almond-shaped nor spherical; moreover it neither looks like a chestnut nor does it taste like one. Even when cooked it still calls to mind the pond where it was born and the mud that nurtured it. Its long tubular stalks—the root-stock vegetates in the slime—

crisscross the bottom mud before rising to the surface, there to disseminate their delightful white flowers, flat leaves, and later the drab green fruit so quick to sprout horns. If not gathered in the nick of time, the fruit will detach itself from the tubular stalk and sink back to the murky depths, to settle down beside the small tench of which, to my way of thinking, it bears a distinct flavour. The following year it will be its turn to sprout and direct the gradual ascent of sleek leaves and white flowers at the end of a pliant tube.

On my ponds an old punt puts out here and there to gather the water caltrops during September-October. Or else a man, nearly always an old man, clad in the remnants of a tattered pair of breeches, will kick off his sabots on the bank before wading breast-high into water that has ever a treacherous appearance, inasmuch as it rises from latent springs in rippling wavelets of alternating warm and cold currents, and is the habitat of little else than stout undulating water weeds that elude one's grasp.

The fragrance of riverside reeds, of spearmint, of eddying, disturbed water mingled with the parlous and pervasive savour of caltrops, these delights are not yet destined to escape, not for this year at any rate, one who has the wits to keep them safe in her Paris room—by denomination a writer increasingly under the dominance of her malady, but each day afforded relief by the faithful memory of her brain and of her subtle senses that in old age have lost none of their cunning.

In anticipation of the time when I shall no longer be able to move, I make no effort to move.

I ride at anchor beneath the blue lantern, which is quite simply a powerful commercial lamp at the end of a lengthy extensible arm, fitted with a blue bulb and a blue paper shade. Though a permanent fixture, it has none the less suggested to my neighbours the name they have chosen to baptise it with—*fanal*—the light that rakes the seas. "Madame Colette, you can't imagine how pretty your lantern looked yesterday, shining through the fog. . . . Oh, but you can't tell me that you make sparing use of your blue lantern! It's on at all hours, in the early morning, at eight, sometimes at seven-thirty even!" There is nothing I can hide from them, not even the moment—at cock-crow, perhaps—when the beam from my lantern casts a blueness over the brown coffee-pot and the white milk-jug. I tend to make less and less distinction between the hours of night and the hours of day, the hour for reading, for writing, for looking about me, all are equally good. The hour for conjecture, for testing my memory! Before long I shall be confusing the hour for work with the hour for conjecture; wondering what Gide can be up to—my enticing Gide, whom I can never see enough or read enough—and fussing over some crazy scheme of mine, will become one and the same concern. One good example of a crazy scheme was my longing to copy the lovely rug which Jean Cocteau had bought for his house in the country. All of a sudden I felt I must have it! But the rug was at Milly! I must have it, I have to have it at once, so I summon it by telephone. I am answered by a chorus of voices: my neighbours in Rue Montpensier become alarmed; Jean Cocteau has been called abroad, Jean Marais is on some film location or other! What matter! Paul-of-the-bookshop (easier to pronounce than Paul Morihien) shall be dispatched to Milly, they'll charter an aeroplane, they'll send the Emperor of the Indies!

At that point I begged that nobody be put to any trouble, insisted that there was no real urgency. Too late: the wheels had been set in motion on my behalf from Beaujolais to Montpensier. Then out of the blue Jean Marais sprang to life before my very eyes, tall enough to brush the ceiling with his orange—no, moonlight blue— no, auburn mop of hair! And what in the world was he trailing along behind him, slung from his shoulder? It looked like some long drag-net.

"Have you come straight in here from a fishing expedition, Jeannot? Sardines, is it, you have there? Or good fresh herring?

"Nothing of the sort, it's *the* rug. Nobody could find the time to go to Milly, Jean's somewhere up in the air between Paris and New York, Paul-of-the-bookshop is busy arranging some book exhibition, so off I hopped there."

A hop of one hundred and twenty kilometres, there and back. He certainly had lost no time, with his seven-league boots. In everything about him there was an air of breath-taking efficiency in carrying out an indisputably urgent commission, in his white rain-coat, his turquoise blue cashmere scarf, his hair rising straight off his head, and the panting mask of his dog Moulouk. How was it possible to confess to Jean Marais that it would not have mattered in the least if nobody had gone to Milly! What reverberated throughout my little room to the exclusion of all else was this haste of his, and in my imagination the sound of the full-tilt gallop along the road, the kid-

napping of the rug, my staircase scaled as readily as the
stairs of a convent thrown open to the Musketeers! Jean
Marais, Jean Marais, hero of countless films and plays,
how admirably your legend fits you, and how splendidly
you live up to it! I told myself that day that I had seen
you playing the lead in *The House of the Fisherman*,
and that in your wake trailed the drag-net, bringing in
with it the smell of seaweed and the glitter of a myriad
opalescent fish scales!

From time to time I have to take stock of what has been
going on in the world of the cinema, so I do go to one
film a year, or two. It is not sufficient. But it is enough
for me, once I have settled down again to the rhythm, to
the black and white of the screen, to find myself
astounded at how much there remains of crude ostentation and simple incongruity in the realm of cinematic
invention and representation. After an enforced absence
over lengthy periods, I ache to say to the screen "Don't
tell me that you are still where you were! What have you
been doing whilst I've been away?" And then I allow
myself to fall under its spell once again. It is so hard to
withhold one's admiration. I forget that we have every
right to demand colour and "audience participation",
and in the end I am content to go away with what I have
retained of my journey to the other side of the world,
of the human conflict, and of my own insatiable curiosity.
Happy come, happy go, like the roan mare in the story
books.

They (the Radiodiffusion people) one day asked Jean Cocteau and myself to record a short conversation in which "we could say what we liked", and "promptly" the radio van arrived outside, and "promptly" Jean was here beside me, perched on the poop of my workaday raft, with the rays of my blue lantern turning his face green.

This culmination of happy coincidences did not prevent Jean and myself from exchanging a glance or two. I was quick to catch the look of apprehension in his deep-set eyes that he must have been aware of in my own. We had to improvise, and I am no good at improvisation. And I feel far from at home with that bell-shaped flower, the campanula—pear, cucumber, or whatever name it goes by —which an insidious hand was already holding out toward us. Too late in life I came into contact with the microphone, with all its paraphernalia that climbs in through the windows, sprawls across the kitchen floor, strangles a small table in its progress down the passage, and coils up close beside me as I lie in bed.

"And how do you feel about it, Jean?"

"Me! I have an unholy horror of the contraption. And at the present moment I'm asleep on my feet. Ever since noon yesterday I've been hard at work, right on through till one o'clock today. What's more, I've had no proper lunch. I'd far rather speak to a thousand faces and a thousand pairs of ears than into this . . . this pumpkin! At last—is all set now?"

"All's ready."

"Then you'd better begin. What are we going to talk about?"

"Anything you like," proposed the young man in charge of the coils.

"But I don't like. So you begin. Suppose we pretend to be taking a stroll in the Garden?"

"On my crippled legs! You make me laugh."

But I was not laughing. Neither was Jean Cocteau. He closed his eyes, hid his face behind his long elegant fingers, and courageously launched forth. I was full of admiration for his diction, his well-timed periods, the variety in tone of this musician-orator. I responded as best I could, but my best was not very good. However, the young man with the campanula was pleased to give us a "perfect!" before he rolled up his coils, detached himself from his calix, and made off, while I pulled back my bench-table close beside me with the crook of my harpoon-stick. Under the stress of emotion Jean's face had gone black and blue under the eyes, and I quickly withdrew my still icy hand from his. We lost no time in concealing our attack of radio fright. I believe mine must have been the worse, since it forecast a whole host of other pitfalls. It gave me advance warning of the voice sticking in the throat, the speck of dust in the tonsils, the unexpected spoonerism. In vain it inveighed against the major be-trayal: for it is all very well, but I have never in my life spoken in such a deep cavernous voice like the one I heard, I have never arrrticulated in such an ultrrra-Burrr-gundian manner! People assure me that I am mistaken, that my voice comes over on the radio just as it sounds in "real life". I shall not dispute the point.

Jean Cocteau comes into my room, and I look at the

time by my cardiac watch, and am amazed: eleven-thirty in the morning! Had it been at night I should have had no cause for surprise. Before I can ask any questions he supplies the answer.

"Yes . . . Can you believe it, but my electricians, camera-men, and carpenters in the studio have just told me they're on strike!"

He contrives to squeeze his long body on to the poop of my raft, folds his arms and legs, and coils up his body so as to expose as much as possible of it to my sun-ray, which will shortly be coming up to noon.

"So what?"

"So nothing. I walked out of the studio."

"A holiday! Calm yourself. It's always like that."

His nose looks at me sideways, in some perplexity.

"To be strictly accurate, it's no longer like that. I've worked like a mad thing for a number of years now. Night, and day, and Sundays. On a tray, on a restaurant table, on the grass in the country, on paper. In the past it was the pressure of work that half-murdered me. Today, I no longer know how to knock off work unless a break has been arranged for me well in advance. Once again I'm being deprived of my poison, and I'm aching in every joint. It's a quarter to twelve. I'm not hungry. I never feel hungry. What is there to do at a quarter to twelve, when one's not working. I've forgotten."

"Stay here with me."

"That I can't do. Stay here with you at a quarter to twelve! It's simply not done."

"Where will you go, then?"

"To be honest, I don't know. I'm going to try to go home."

From the tone in which he says this, he might be embarking on some great adventure.

As the wind was coming from the right quarter, I could hear the bells for the midnight mass; then, a little later, I listened on the radio to the mass by J. S. Bach. Pauline had elected to go to Saint-Eustache, whence she returned disappointed. "The crowd was far too great and it was perishing cold. And it wasn't a proper Market crowd. For me, midnight mass must be made up of Market people." On this sibylline utterance she left the room, to see the New Year in off Auvergne cheese and a pint of champagne. I could not have chosen better myself, had I felt the least bit hungry. But I simply had no appetite for such a repast, no more than I used to have, it must be added, for my old pre-war New Year's Eve revels. How many were the *Réveillons* in the good old days that found us grouped together in some famous restaurant—the men in white ties, the women in low evening dresses—along with great editors-in-chief and big industrialists, even with deputies and ministers who considered themselves great!

We also used to see the New Year in at Madame Hessèle's among the notable artists of the day: Vuillard, Dunoyer de Segonzac, Luc-Albert Moreau and others. This was already an improvement, despite the early stages being a little too formal under the military discipline of our hostess, white-haired and dressed in white. She would have reminded us of Madame Aubernon, had that good lady not been so far removed from us. But what a lot of good painters there were to give full rein to their high spirits!

Elsewhere, in other studios, I remember how the furniture used to be moved out of and brought into the room to allow for table space for the oysters, the turkey, and the foie gras. The first wave of champagne was rough and far too cold, the second already too warm. The *consommé en tasses* was too clear, the caviar too black.

In every restaurant little multicoloured cotton balls, guarantees of reckless gaiety, began to rain down as soon as the soup came in, and into the soup, as often as not! Oh, I have a store of memories of even more enjoyable réveillons! But tonight they are dormant, and I am lying down.

A tour of my quarter, by car. Apart from the butchers' shops, apart from the silver paper and the apples, I search in vain for the quondam opulence of the *premier arondissement*. Once again I find, and can still appreciate, the stylishness with which—fine artists that they are—the gentlemen of the butchers' shops dress their meat. As he chops, cuts, slices, trims, shapes, or threads through the string, a butcher is as good a sight to watch as a dancer or mime. A Parisian butcher, that goes without saying. With his golden bang of hair atop his forehead, his cheek ruddy as the dawn and his ear pink as a rose, with his apron strings tied in the approved style and spotted here and there with just the proper amount of blood-stains, I can tell you, Madame, that a Parisian butcher is well worth your passing glance; worth more, perhaps, than that.

My promenade, were I to allow myself to make one, would turn into a melancholy pilgrimage. In Rue de

Valois, under a lovely balcony, that famous restaurant of old—*Au Bœuf à la Mode*—used to hold sway. Today the balcony is still there. The succulent beef, the excellent way of making sauces, of cooking carrots, bacon, and calves' foot, are no more.

> *Irai-je voir le bœuf gras?*
> *Irai-je voir ma maîtresse?*
> *D'un côté l'amour me presse.*
> *Mais le bœuf a tant d'appas!*

Did Gavarni himself compose that quatrain? It appears as the caption to one of his enchanting drawings, in which he has grouped a posse of "Lions", excessively tight-waisted, and ladies of the town, with sloping shoulders like Rhenish wine bottles and dark Andalusian eyes.

Next door to the *Bœuf*, let a tear be shed for the *Pâtisserie Flammang*, famed for its éclairs and Neapolitan ices, and for the departed glories of its glass panelling of the Restoration period, painted with garlands. The Flammangs were reduced to penury by selling their delicate cream-tarts and puff-pastries which simply ran away with the best butter.

I mourn the loss of the good proprietors themselves as much as that of their good confectionery. All among the flowered panels, as pleasing to the eye as those of the Grand Véfour, lived a family of ladies in black, the eldest of whom had her place at the desk. A younger sister supervised the faultless service of the waitresses, while a second generation, represented by a young woman of unobtrusive colouring, enquired after the health of the customers as she wrapped up a tartlet, a *saint-honoré*, or

a *savarin*—" Deliciously moist, is it not, Madame? "—in
its conical tent of tissue-paper. A little girl who never
opened her mouth made out fair copies of the bills close
beside the cash desk. Flammang's is now a co-op painted
in bright green. The ravishing glass panels have found
their way to the Carnavalet Museum. A fat lot of good
that will do us—and them!

All of which is none too cheerful. If I failed to stand
up for myself, I should become as grumpy as any old
dotard. But I do stand up for myself, I do myself well on
the black market. I go gadding off to a shop in my wheel-
chair, a place known only to myself and a few others and
presided over by a dazzling young lady. For nowadays
you will no longer find "black" establishments run by
tight-lipped shrews or gruff, sardonic young persons.
Cordiality is now the order of the day. As to its where-
abouts, you had far better make enquiries from Simone
Berrian, or Cécile Sorel, but do not expect me to reveal
to you the spot where I was once lost in admiration of
the pair of them, each as agile as the other, perched like
a couple of wagtails atop precipitous chests, plunging
their hands into dingy drawers as though they were bran-
pies, from which with shrieks of triumph they fished out
a varied booty of mealy camemberts, a small bag of rancid
nuts, a pair of espadrilles, a powdery cake of Marseilles
soap, as well as other treasure-trove which they seemed
to value far in excess of its true worth and utility. To
such a pitch, that at one moment, like birds gorged on a
surfeit of black currants, they neglected to notice, from
their perch on high, what a fine display of their pretty
legs they were exhibiting. None of this was lost on a
young man, the apparent owner of the store, whose looks

betrayed his feelings, the entire stock of his sentiments. But for him I should never have realised how disinterested the running of a black market business can become, as much under the influence of passion as of nameless reverie!

But here I am speaking of times past and gone: all the actors on that particular stage must long since have returned to the paths of legitimate trading—all, that is, save myself.

 VIII

28 January, 1948.

Iɴ the room which no device could ever sufficiently heat I was born laboriously on January the 28th, 1873, and I caused my mother much pain in her travail. For close on forty-eight hours she struggled as only women in the pangs of childbirth know how to fight. The women about her lost their heads and forgot to feed the fire in the grate. By dint of her cries and anguish my mother drove me from her womb, but since I had entered the world blue and silent, nobody thought it worth while to bother about me.

There was very little of charm or comfort about that room. Curtains of flowered print, mounted on an old-fashioned triangular frame, were draped over the widely separated beds of my parents. A curious little squat boot-cupboard stood in the embrasure of the window opening on the street and could be used as a seat. The glass-fronted wardrobe of three unequal sections was made of Brazilian rosewood, lined with polished thuya, and always struck me as over-decorative and out of place.

The twenty-eighth of January came and went fifteen times without witnessing any change in the room where I was born half-choked, but showing a determined will to live and even to live long, for I have just reached my seventy-fifth birthday—an anniversary the friends around me persist in calling "a great day". It is they, let me say, who have made it so. They have given me so many things.

They have given me flowers, fruits and sweets, and offered their congratulations on my seventy-five years from morn till eve. They have eulogised me in the papers, to an extent that has led me to think that I have nothing but friends in the world. They have sent me letters and telegrams and photographs: "You can see how pretty our little girl is at three months! We have called her Françoise." And a sheaf of picture-postcards! "Madame, this is simply a little Swiss cat wishing you a happy birthday; she is seven months old and quite white." To which, kitten or pretty poppet, the palm?

They have sent me the first violet of the year: "Jacqueline had the idea of going to see whether there was not one in flower under the sheltered briar, and such enough there was one!"

Anacreon (Richard) has written to me: "Since there are not seventy-five candles in our house, nor in the whole Rue de Seine, I am sending you seventy-five carnations, one for each year."

A bottle from Bordeaux has travelled all the way here in safety, bearing on its little paunch its vintage year—1873, the year of my birth—and its cobweb of precious dust. Like me, it was kept on its back till dinner-time on the twenty-eighth of January; again like me, bless me if it hadn't retained something of its fire and colour, together with a pleasant suspicion of violets, and the Mouton wine which it brought me was sleeping peacefully on its bed of lees, from which we awakened it with care and gratitude! And my dearest friend put a circlet of gold round my wrist—my favourite metal whether it comes in the shape of a bracelet, a medal, or the links of a chain. There were many other presents too, fit between them all to choke me with emotion; there was the blue-black hyacinth embroidered on a gilt-edged card, and the pink hyacinth from Rosa, and the snowdrops from two little working-girls, who did not leave their names and made off at once; a splendid array of fruit from Pauline: " I could not have borne to let anyone else give Madame finer fruit, today of all days! " There was the spray of orchids from my daughter.

" I bet it must have cost you your shirt to buy me this spray! "

" Oh, no Maman, don't you worry. You know perfectly well I never wear a shirt."

And from my neighbours there were flowers without end for my small vases, as well as a painting of a rose by Redouté, and a wonderful sausage of purest pork for cooking.

And two American ladies have put in my hands two of those American parcels, one from the East and one from the West, which gladden the eyes no less than the palate; for the silver paper, glazed cartons, flowered wrappings, and glossy containers double the attraction of the plums, gâteaux, pure wheaten flour, Malaga grapes and the transparent sweetmeats they contain.

" I'll swap my share of powdered milk for your empty box," was the offer made to his sister by a little boy paying me a neighbourly visit.

"Don't be silly! I'm not such a fool," answered his sister. "Not even if you throw in your mint chocolates as well! "

And then the full jereboam of champagne that I had!

And the zariba of red azaleas raised all round me by my fellow members of the Académie Goncourt! And the newspapers splashed with affectionately possessive references to "Our Colette"! How I enjoy being a joint estate! Marguerite Moreno's warm voice spoke to me on the radio, borne over the air on its incomparable rhythm, rich in a great variety of overtones, with every now and then an accent of affection and tenderness—at the very moment when I was not listening. Marguerite did her best to console me for not having heard her: "It makes no difference, ma Colette. We'll have a repeat performance, you and I, in seventy-five years' time." Oh, Marguerite, I would like it well enough at this moment, now, when I know what it would be like, when to my divan-raft, loaded down with presents and lit by a blue lantern, I have welcomed a disorderly array, such warmth and affection, and a wealth of smiles and tears not unworthy of youth itself.

Only a very small remnant of the younger generation of my sex can nowadays be numbered among my intimates. I should have more, if I let them come. But I dread them. It is in the course of nature for declining strength to be scared of up-and-coming new forces. Severity in passing judgment on the latter is not the former's lot, even supposing we possessed it.

The cocksure approach employed by the very young to hurt our feelings will always be quicker off the mark than our judicial utterances whenever we attempt, unsuccessfully, to temper enthusiasm by a little fairness.

I have never suffered from lack of curiosity. Why

should I go to the lengths, then, in face of the young of either sex, of denying the attraction that other forms of first appearances hold for me?

Curiosity is seldom a root cause of ill will, yet how is one to make best use of it once the days of temperamental effrontery are behind one? I have no fear of my women friends; but I fear a friend's daughter, even more so the daughter of a friend's daughter. The children who do not come to see me but who write me letters lay claim to great timidity. If they mean timidity about literary matters, which may lead them to seek advice and tips, I can well believe them. But as to timidity of other kinds, it is for me and those of my age to feel it, almost to the point of painful intensity.

I do not go out of my way to offer encouragement to my youthful friends. I do not go so far as to drive them away. They must find me lacking in conversation, since the truth is that for them I have very little to give, and I am left with nothing but a consuming itch to ask questions when I take a hand in the most exhausting of all pleasures. When I am alone with those already settled in a profession, I never end without winning from them what I best like, something of the romance of their profession. I like it the more for the fact that they do not seem to realise how moving they are when giving expression to their hopes and fears. Their pathos emerges, wrapped up as it is in the most commonplace expressions our language contains, in expletives, in hideously accurate computations voiced without a trace of emotion. Yet between them and me stretches an ever widening and worsening gulf, unbridgeable by friendly familiarity and still less by expressions of good will, in which they have but little belief. Curiosity—which in their self-infatuation they consider fair enough—serves my turn better, as does that mischievous gift for reading the heart, inherited from Sido, to which I have playful recourse. I make only playful use of it, never in the spirit of triumph. Let me stress that for all my advanced years some of my amusements are perfectly innocent.

My youthful girl friends and I find it easier to cope with topics uninvolved with intimacy, such as the theatre and its concern with dramatic art, the cinema as a means of getting on in the world, bibliophily considered as a business opening. In these fields of human activity, they beat me hands down. Young people of both sexes know all there is to know about these everyday outlets. The pleasure I derive from being astonished fills them with pride and makes them talkative; what is more, both sexes turn out to be on common ground in their pursuit of special editions, autographs and dedications, in their passion for " Grangerising " or extra-illustrating " original issues ", to the neglect of fine old albums bound with a clasp-lock, and other " Golden Treasuries ". Crazes of this sort are curiously interrelated with a strong family feeling, long thought to be a thing of the past; not long ago I signed a copy of *Le pur et l'impur* presented to me by a bibliophile aged five-and-a-half, whose far-sighted mother had brought him along for the purpose.

In so far as I can make contact with such remote creatures, I find our young French girls to be lively and ambitious, but troubled in mind. Their self-confidence is merely a façade. They are mettlesome but quickly discouraged, like draught-horses that are not properly fed. They bear the traces of an inner conflict that has barely troubled their conscience, as it were a painless wound. Among my acquaintances are three sisters and a female cousin. One of them has devoted herself to music, in spite of all and in her own despite, and nothing will induce her to give it up. When music decides . . . Another paints, but before another year is out will not, I believe, still be painting. The third is a dancer, and every day grows thinner. A question of good beefsteak, this!

The female cousin has snatched at a small opening on the stage, and is shortly to make her début in a piece in which all the characters are eighteen-year-olds; meanwhile she is doing, as the saying goes, "a spot of filming". She does not say "a spot", however, but "a sport", being still child enough to enjoy the language of mystery.

Her name is Catherine. Were she not called Catherine, her name would be Chantal, or Dominique. Her parents are lacking in originality, foresight, and historical sense. She comes to see me because her mother, who is only twenty years younger than myself, says to her at intervals: "Go and pay a call on Madame Colette, be very polite to her and do not tire her out."

"Can I ask her to put in a good word for me with Jean Cocteau?" asks Catherine insidiously.

"Yes, but make it sound as if it came quite naturally into the course of the conversation."

That only goes to show that Catherine has been well brought up. She comes into my room and, before untying under her chin the scarf which makes a hat unnecessary and keeps a permanent wave unruffled, she will say "Madame Colette, would you be so kind as to say a word for me to Jean Cocteau?"

"Yes, if you will tell me about the dress you are to wear in the first act of your forthcoming play."

"The dresses for it are excellent, as is always the case," she obliges with a specious air of condescension. "If I get nothing worse than a 'sport of bad news' in the papers from Jean-Jacques Gautier, I'll be able to live that down. Especially as my dress in the first act is in a ribbed aquamarine ottoman silk. A small bunch of mauve auriculas at the waist and a great white forehead."

"A great white what?"

"White forehead."

"Where on earth . . ."

"Why, on the forehead."

"You've not got a vast forehead, thank the Lord."

"Oh, I'll enlarge it with an electric razor!"

"How horrible!"

"It's indispensable. It's the hallmark of purity, especially in the case of a *jeune fille*. Besides everyone—every woman, that is—has a great white forehead."

"I am only too well aware of it. And 'on the day' you will also, I suppose, display in all their nakedness the little bare bumps behind your ears?"

"Why, of course!"

"Indecency can go no further. Have you never looked in a glass to see the back of your ears? In which case don't you know that even in the prettiest woman, or the prettiest child, they are a plague spot? That ever since little girls have had their hair screwed up into two tight-plaited pigtails, like lobsters' tails, they have looked hideous in back view? That behind the ears, napes, and children's skinny necks, are places in the process of formation that should be kept hidden by a providential

growth of vegetation, light, golden or brown? That ever
since women took to sporting what Marguerite Moreno
calls 'the vast encyclopedic forehead of a waiter' com-
patability has ceased to be possible between your face and
the hazardous frivolity of your hats, between the desert
of forehead and the neat wavy garland that sweeps back
off it, between the barren earth and the bird perched
above it, between the blasted heath and the arch features
of a girl of eighteen like you?"

"There is nothing arch about me," Catherine interrupted stiffly. "And it was Jouvet himself who once told
me that my future lay in wronged women."

"Jouvet and his wronged women! That may be . . ."

"Oh!" Catherine began, blushing with expectancy.

But with a gesture I cut short her budding and
evident hopes. "That is not a promise, Catherine. Go
on!"

"But so far I've told you nothing."

So irreproachable a repartee, so just a criticism of my
flow of words, laid me flat. A very palpable hit!

"There is still some Swiss chocolate left in that box,
so do help yourself. What's new in town?"

"That the fringe is coming back into favour. Very soon
we shall all be looking like Lautrecs. You'll like that,
Madame Colette!"

I turned on her the glowering eye of an old warrior
and deluged her with a shower of truisms dear to my
heart, touching on the comparison of a head of hair to
foliage, and the female face to fruit; I even went so far,
to put Catherine on her mettle, as to bring to her notice
the superb, curl-bedecked, young foreheads of Martine
Rouchard and Dominique Blanchar. A moment later I

was in full cry as I recalled the raven kiss-curls that so enhanced the wan and cat-like face of Rachilde. And I had good reason, for Catherine was looking at the time by my cardiac watch. Her sole reaction was to banish from her face every hair that had strayed from her ash-blonde tresses with a thoroughness which might have been taken for an impertinence, to excuse herself on the grounds of "her" rehearsal, and make an effective exit, after an "au revoir" very prettily mimed and spoken, the *sine qua non* of good manners, as they are called. As if good manners turned on a gesture and an intonation! This fair-haired, sharp-angled Catherine intimidates me, but I make an impression on her.

She did not take her leave before offering to help me: "The rug? Your cushions? Are the sticks within your reach?" A fresh-cheeked girl, sophisticated, hard as nails, courageous, wrapped up in herself, and perhaps, in her heart of hearts, a romantic. I like the element of contradiction in her, her pleasantly acid personality, the rebellious spirit in so young a bud. It seemed to me that once man—the hand, the mouth, the body of a man—had touched her, the world around her would be aware of it . . . myself the first, naturally. Was I like that, I wonder, at her age! My memory is not clear, but I vividly recall my shudder of repugnance when I was very young—does Catherine feel the same with me?—at the touch of old people, and the wild delight with which at the end of the visit I made good my escape from Mme de Cadalvène or Mme Bourgneuf, old ladies of over eighty, whom age and infirmity kept glued to the window panes on the well-worn rim of their constricted nests. I avoided the clutches of the small paralysed hand, crumpled as a claw, that offered me a stick of Vichy barley-sugar. It needed every ounce of Sido's authority to force me to pick up a detested silk scarf from beside a pair of lifeless feet shod in felt slippers. Equally detestable to me was a certain china cup, and also a certain cushion of black woven horsehair. . . . It was I, therefore, and not Catherine, who heard a quiet voice saying "You must be very kind to Mme Bourgneuf." But in those days I had eyes for details only, the very things that are now, inescapable as doom, gathering on every side of me, to wit the pair of crutches, the vicuna shawl, and my spectacles.

Oh . . . Pauline, fetch me quick my blue dressing-gown, yes, yes, the new one, and the rose-pink foulard, and the scent-spray, and the bowl of cyclamen from my table—my powder-box as well. I ought to have been given all that, goodness knows, just before my young visitor arrived. I look a perfect fright.

Rare are the days on which I receive no presents. Let us understand each other; I mean, almost exclusively, presents from those who know me well, and know how to cater for what I call my insatiable appetite. Today I have received the first chestnuts, small, hard, and dark brown, finished off with a broad, light birth-mark and three stiff little hairs at the tip, showing that they have only just reached maturity. They come from a wood quite close to Paris, some seven or eight kilometres away, which I can see from here: a steep, wooded slope, sparsely planted with ill-tended oak and fir and chestnut. A mere slit in the road beckons the passer-by, uninvitingly, to come upon a wooden chalet, set on brick-work that is losing all its mortar. What can this *dacha* be doing there? Hush! We must respect the cerebral repose of two over-worked doctors—"my doctors" I call them—who cut themselves off from the world on Sundays. On one occasion I was able to follow them into their retreat, where they gave proof of a blissful resemblance to all children who ever hid in a wood, lit a camp fire, ate off a paper plate, drank from the same bottle, and they listened to the silence perforated only by the whistle of a train and the twitter of a tomtit. Having tracked them to their lair but once, I know that squirrels frolic high above them and that one blazing hot day they covered the escape of a large grass snake. Their view consists of unpeopled tracts of the Ile-de-France and the surrounding countryside, both scoured by railway lines, both speckled with small villas, but serene and all the more expansive for the sky above them.

It is but seldom that I can accompany these two am-bitious women, who dream of putting behind them con-sulting room and laboratory for a few hours. Their several skills long since outdistanced what the untutored mind can grasp, yet they gaze in wonder at the mimetic spider simulating a pink pearl among the pink heather flowers, at the rotund puff-ball, that unspotted egg laid when the nights are freshening. They know what it is I long to see and bring it back to me: a hatful of ripening chestnuts and edible mushrooms, to appease my greed, and for my pleasure a variety of wild flowers, the matted head of the rose-gall, together with three unripe chestnuts, tight-packed in a single husk. The husk is beginning to split and through the cleavage can be seen the gleam of the three light mahogany fruits. By a trick of my peculiarly tenacious memory, I can close my hand over the ligneous twig-tip that held suspended this lovely green sea-urchin and then all I have to do is to clamber up as far as the solid wall of leaves to reach the neighbouring pines. Further on it is all sand, birch trees, heather and bramble-bushes laden with berries. Just let me go there, I shall not lose myself. Shut the door of my bedroom. I need nobody to guide me on my walk. All that I needed were these three chestnuts, packed tight in a single half-split-open husk. Au revoir, au revoir, I may be a little late for dinner.

Jean Marais has given me a landscape, painted in oils on a small panel. In the foreground, on the bark of a great branching tree, he has inscribed my name. Beyond this tree, the fields spread out and lose themselves in the distant sea near Arcachon, and on its azure blue I am lying.

The stage vies with the screen for the allegiance of this tall, stern-visaged archangel, and the stage is fighting a losing battle. To visit me he has to fold the wings he has battered against the sets and burnt in the "sunlights". He does not complain, he calls his angelic patience into play. But often he tries to make good his escape. Sometimes he succeeds, by availing himself of a little entresol tunnel with a very low ceiling. Sitting with knees up to his chin and elbows to his sides, stiff all over and happy, bent over a panel no bigger than a cigar box, he painted for me a splendid section of immensity. After which he came to give it me, embraced me, did not jar my crippled legs, did not upset my working-table, or send my spectacles flying. He shoved his forehead—his "Beast's" forehead—his tawny mane of hair and his puckered nostrils, between my ear and my shoulder, without in the least bit crushing me, expressing in a single caress affection and strength. Meanwhile at the back of my room Moulouk, who owns allegiance to Jean Marais alone, who ages when he is away and grows young under a look from his master, turned away his head and refused to say goodday to me.

Last week I became a receiver of stolen fruit. "A lady of my quarter" brought it me, speaking in a whisper but bubbling over with the story. A slightly wrinkled apple clung tenaciously to a bare twig in her hand. "It's a Japanese apple," the story-teller murmured. "It comes from the gardens at the foot of the Eiffel Tower. Somebody stole it for Madame Colette, just when the gardener was lighting his pipe." I gave myself up to an incontinent dream that the Tower Gardens, hitherto unexplored, were really a paradise of exotic trees given over to mango, chcrimoya, or pineapple—perhaps, who can tell!—to the gigantic fruit of the jacquier.

For hardly had I got the apple to myself when it began to exhale a half quince, half apple odour which I can only qualify as Circean, enchanted and enchanting, and so potent that even the atmosphere in the next room—more often than not so redolent of fried onions—was cleansed by it. In a matter of minutes the stairwell, Mecca to their too assiduous lordships the tom cats, smelt of nothing but the strongest apples and quince mitigated by lemon juice, magnified twenty thousandfold, all three of them. Losing all sense of proportion, the fragrance continued on its way down to the ground floor, where it woke up the lady of the book shop who, two fingers to her dreamy forehead, took herself to task for having allowed her preserves to overcook.

When night fell I invited the stolen apple to sleep close beside me, in the embrasure of the window, for all that midnight and the waning moon might quadruple its propensities, and though my dearest friend from his adjoining room might try his best to dissuade me by crying aloud, calling down countless maledictions on Japan, apple-trees, the dangers of toxic exhalations, and pilferers from public gardens. But since he is well mannered enough never to raise his voice when driven to cry aloud, I did not hear him, and trustfully embarked on a wave of sleep almost immediately fraught with dreams and delusions such as had never before assailed me on my divan-raft.

Even then the last word was still left in dispute between myself and the origin of evil. Since the weather was clement for so late in the season and I was able to sleep "in the garden", I had only to make a long arm to take the apple in my hand and cast it forth. I then noticed through the balustrades of my window, for the garden below was already whitening with the dew at dawn, that a long cat had sprung out from the spindlewood hedge and was chasing after the apple. But no sooner had he caught up with it than he retched violently and at once began covering it over with earth, according it thus the fate it doubtless deserved as a fugitive from some dubious Eden. Then he made off with a cat's measured step, supposedly satisfied that he had exorcised the malignant spell by the potent means of ashes, vomit and oblivion.

I have long since discarded the habit of examining an
envelope before opening it, or scrutinising the handwriting before perusing it. This habit persists only in the
case of solitary persons, of those deprived of letter-writing
friends. Too soon I took to massacring the envelopes,
sometimes to the detriment of their contents. André
Lecerf would tell me that herein lay a revealing feature
of my character, but not, I fear, a very flattering one.

Why do I not make use of a paper-cutter, so much more
convenient and more elegant? Ah, there's the rub! Why,
among my total collection of paper-cutters, can I never
find one to serve me faithfully? In the good old days I
used to buy them ten or twelve at a time, of white wood,
at station bookstalls. Thereafter they would disappear, all
ten or twelve of them. The point of my pencil insists on
breaking and flies up into my face. The pull or push-bell
has become a stage accessory, a wire without a voice. My
watch, as I have said, is cardiac. The evening paper simply
melts away, disappears. All these are family misfortunes,
and are hereditary; my father could only control the mad
antics of *Le Temps* by sitting on it. What's more, the
human paperweight was hardly adequate. What use do
people find for a piece of india-rubber? Or for a ruler?
The various chattels designed to make work easier have
never stood me in good stead; but my form of spite,
which is simply to do without them, has theirs beaten.
I almost persuade myself that I am now in the course of
achieving a measure of independence. And high time too!
The times of postal deliveries are exciting moments

indeed in a writer's life! Mangled the envelopes, lacerated the letters from strangers—oh, if only they wrote more briefly!—an unavowed appetite, the hunger for the society of one's fellows which makes one ask for more, plays havoc with their missives, and at the same time calls forth an " Ouf! " or " Is that all? " What is left of my interest in graphological studies leaves me grumbling and offended at the sight of certain handwriting. If every script paints a portrait, I object to each single written page bearing the speaking likeness of a disagreeable grimace.

Between the ages of six and nine, I wrote quickly and badly, as did all children who were taught only the slanting hand, called " English ", which involved keeping the shoulders straight in line and the right index finger humped. About my thirteenth year, to my great good fortune, a lively, exacting young woman was promoted to the post of teacher in my village, who said, as she bent over my copy books, " Your handwriting is vile. Why? "

I was not expecting the final monosyllable and could think of nothing to say.

"Yes, why? Your writing is inexcusable. I give you a week in which to improve it. That's ample time. Take to using a Flamant No. 2. nib, which has a broad point. That will help you to form your letters slowly and clearly, and more upright. Has it never struck you that to be illegible is an act of grave discourtesy? I will not tolerate such an offence against myself."

The results of a wigging such as that were not slow in taking effect. Fifty years later I tried out a similar gambit on Claude Chauvière, whose handwriting positively repelled the reader. Flowing to the extent of being formless (a feature not, alas! without significance), negligent of loops and lines, omitting any couplings, her script was like a streaming banner struggling to free itself; to decipher it caused me as much annoyance as discomfort, so I treated Claude like a badly brought-up child.

Being both proud and quick-tempered, she went red and pale in turns. "Madame, I shall spare you the sight of my distasteful writing and the company of a person of no education!"

At that I called her a noodle, a word she drank in as the highest compliment, and her face suddenly dissolved in tears and laughter. Now I am very happy to come upon her and her careless hand once again, in the margins and the interlinings of that gale of exaltation and perplexity of soul which I have in proof and to which she gave the title *Manuscript found in a Monastery*.

The magnificent, harmonious handwriting of Germaine Beaumont brings cheer to eye and mind. In it can be seen and read all the vigorous merits of that great writer of fiction, and even one extra for good measure: I mean a sort of noble disdain, to which her talent, and the independence that she has won for herself, give her the right.

My own writing is not ugly, though I say it who shouldn't. It is like myself, a little stocky, the upstrokes full and rounded, and legible. I may as well pay myself a small compliment every now and again.

It is by no means easy to rid ourselves of the idea that the time of a postal delivery—especially the first morning delivery—is a time of hope, surprise, and reward. There is animosity in our love of the bundle of scribbled envelopes when still fastened down, then opened, then thrown away. We stop loving it as soon as it holds no more secrets, no more confidences, no more endearments, as soon as it becomes prolix, or degraded by consorting with prospectuses, advertisements for patent medicines, book catalogues and cards from galleries.

Our closest friends, when far removed from us, are the only ones who write us letters with a maximum of reserve and a minimum of news about themselves, remaining silent about their own troubles and concerned entirely with ours—let me particularise and say " with me " and my arthritis : they have discovered an osteopath who . . . a radiologist whom they . . . They quote the case of a miraculous cure, a thermal spring whose . . .

This has the immediate effect of bringing out the worst in my character, since I had anticipated reading an account of their journey, the events of their stay, the exact number of teeth cut by their small daughter, the exact height of the floods in their district—in short, their news. Have none of my friends, my dearest friend included, the least idea of what interests me?

I console myself with the remainder of my post—the letters written to me by strangers. Other than having the good luck to happen upon the peculiarly French grace of writing good letters, I may yet come upon something to astonish me. For people ask me for things which I had never supposed to be at all in my line, for instance " a trustworthy person who could look after a lady of advanced years ". And again ". . . if it is not an impertinence, a decent man, grocers' assistant type, who would accept comfortable post in a town of middling importance. I take the liberty of asking you this, Madame Colette, since everyone knows that you are renowned for your knowledge of the world."

Certainly, Madame! Perhaps not exactly to include the life of a grocer's assistant; but "everyone knows"—I like that "everyone" which gives me self-confidence—that a request for advice about the ailment of a pet does not frighten me, and that I do not throw into the waste-paper basket the story of the caged canaries, set free for reasons of economy, that became crossed with house sparrows and, two years later, are still producing offspring with a small yellow feather showing here and there in their plumage, and with the suggestion of a trill in their throats. I do not tear up the account of a domestic tabby who by dint of love and patience finally induced a handsome, suspicious wild cat, step by step, quivering with exhaustion, to enter the house in the woods. Nor do I throw away the drawings of children. If I were to follow my own inclinations, I would throw away nothing. I do my best to follow my own inclinations as little as possible and to husband my harsh words for anything evil that may come my way in search of strength and encouragement, for the momentary itch that goes by the name of vocation, for the proliferating novel, the literature that loses its way, and for bibliophily in its lazy and primitive form: "Madame, I am leaving my copy with you, and tomorrow I shall return to pick it up enriched by a dedication from yourself." You find the formula somewhat summary? I am not the author of it, I would have you know.

Not all the young bibliomaniacs are quite so . . . succinct. Are they mistaken in taking such liberties? Possibly, since once my initial fit of spleen against the hard, businesslike methods of youth is over, we sign, we respond! However cross they make us, we never feel we are entirely free or quit of them. A single start of refusal brings me up sharp before the most legitimate claim they have on us—the claim on what they call our experience. They need advice and criticism. They want, like my little Yniold, not only " to go and say something to somebody ", but to listen with attentive ear to a voice that will speak to them of themselves.

Children and young people, you who make bold to write to me and in the very first lines tell me of your "timidity ", have you never envisaged the possibility of my timidity being greater than your own? I seek protection, I remain silent, I fear you. I try, but without either naming you or betraying your confidence, to laugh you out of this crazy business of writing to an old woman as if she had no option but to perform a crazy act herself— answer you. Since I cannot do less, I read you, and with scrupulous care. But I have a well-founded suspicion that those who are worst afflicted with the itch to write are not the predestined favourites of literature. Yet to tell them as much . . . I feel that I have neither the right nor the inclination to do so!

Let us, if you will bear with me, read over together some of the shorter letters, which have to my ear an imperturbable note of complacency and fruitless childishness about them. In the first one I catch an overtone of Marguerite Moreno and her businesslike method of answering letters, with something of her gentle raillery.

" Madame Colette, I am much inconvenienced by the death of Madame Moreno, since it has deprived me of the chance of meeting her. This lady had been very kind, she had promised to receive me and to give me favourable *notices in the papers. For I have the gift of comic writing, and people of my acquaintance tell me that my essays and light verse are striking. One day when I telephoned Mme Moreno, I told her that it would be advisable not to put off publishing them too long since I am sixty-nine years old; but she told me that, on the contrary my age would be an additional attraction. Seeing that she has just died, I take the liberty of addressing myself to you, etc., etc. . . ."*

"*Madame Colette, I wonder if you remember me! When you were once staying at X, in 1904 it was, I was the little girl of seven who used to run errands. Since that time, I have married and we have suffered many misfortunes. Things are beginning to look up a bit, but we are still wanting for a number of little things. So I thought of you to write to, and if you know anyone who would let us have for nothing a motor-car that is due to be scrapped. My husband is very clever with his hands and he would be sure to know how to make something of it. Thanking you in advance, dear Madame Colette, etc., etc. . . ."*

Another one? Let us take one more, in my opinion the most unexpected of the lot.

"*Madame, I should like to put some of your writings into verse, among them* La Maison de Claudine. *Spontaneously I make you this offer, to superimpose on your rhythm my own strictly poetic versification.*

If, as I hope, you like this idea, perhaps you would

*also like to write the preface? I should find your advice
useful on a number of points (publisher, typeface, method
of sale, and so on) . . . I enclose a few samples, which
I consider representative of my work."*

Believe it or not, these things do happen, just like that.
In what spirit should letters of this kind be read? Is
there anything to be found in them other than calm self-
assurance, with above all an astounding ignorance of real
life and, in contradistinction, the secret cult of the self
and the crying need for publicity?

Would not you fall in love, as I do myself, with those
who advise me for my good? Not all of them wish me
well, but to one who lacks self-confidence, their assurance
is like a slap on the back.

*"Madame Colette, reading is our greatest pleasure;
but we do not conceal from you the fact that we find
your stories of days gone by a little fatiguing, we should
prefer something more of our own day. We do not scruple
to write to you, for what we have to say may be of some
service to you, etc., etc. . . ."*

*"Madame Colette, my sister and I enjoyed reading
your last book. Do, please, give us some more stories
about your childhood, they are much the most amusing.
As to your talks on the wireless, you ought not to read
them out as you do; you should talk naturally, as though
you were having a conversation with yourself, etc.,
etc. . . ."*

"Your 'Souvenirs' are a bit colourless, a bit lacking in go. What is required is more emotion, more tenderness, in your dialogues with your dearest friend. On the one hand too lifeless, on the other too literary, and marred by insincerity as well. Surely there were better and more important things to say. Take it from a fellow-author who has been prevented by ill health from continuing in his profession, etc., etc. . . ."

Which of them to believe? If only I had twenty or thirty years more to live, I should end by reaping some advantage from all this disinterested advice, contradictory as so much of it is.

My object in quoting it is not to offend but to disclose by what methods a reader gets into touch with an author, to the point of fulfilling some imperative need. I believe there is no effective way of escaping his commandeering method. I also believe, after being thoroughly trained for nearly half a century to his arbitrary requirements, to the mad lack of restraint that guides the pens of lonely women, men with obsessions, and those monomaniacs who persist in asking questions, that I prefer their indiscretion to their silence.

" Madame,

" I send you my life's work; it consists of my impressions and opinions of the books I have read. I have left a blank page between the title and the text, and would ask you to be so kind as to write a preface on this. I shall call for the manuscript in a week's time. Believe me . . . etc., etc. . . .

" P.S. Please make the preface as long as possible."

May I never see God if I am lying, as we say where I come from! The weighty manuscript had been sent by registered post and at the cost of 146 francs to the sender.

"*Madame,*

"*I am thirteen and a half years old. All my life I have been obsessed by a craving to write. People have always told me that I have plenty of talent. But I have hesitated. And now I think it is too late to take such a serious step. My parents tell me that I must continue with my studies, but I have little interest in them. Would you oblige me, Madame, by giving me your opinion . . . etc., etc. . . .*"

The underlining of "all my life" and "always" is mine. As I read them I thought of the little boy-acrobat who rode his bicycle round and round the mosaic pavement at Chartres making dizzy figures of eight, with his hands off the handle-bars. I asked his bearded grandfather who was watching over him how old the child might be.

"Four and a half."

"Four and a half! And he rides like that!"

"Oh!" said the proud grand-parent, "he learnt when he was quite small."

I admire child gymnasts, but I am a little afraid of child writers. To start with, there are too many of them. Then who in the world would not be afraid of a child's vigour and ease of movement through the impenetrable? He lacks only the vocabulary to be our equal when the passion to write comes upon him. I could give the name, at any rate the pseudonym she has chosen to write under, of more than one girl of fifteen whose literary baggage already comprises a slim volume of poems, two plays, three if not more novels, and *Memoirs* (*sic*). There is the same facility among boys. Of course I feel no pressing hurry to form an opinion on so many youthful works, confided to me as they are without my consent. But I still retain my faculty for astonishment, even if it should only be for youthful writers' attempts to exploit their own novelty. Sometimes, it is true, they conceal their identity, but they never forget to state their age. *" Madame, I am thirteen, fourteen, fifteen years old . . ."* Do their parents, tutors and schoolteachers call them " little fiends, exclusively addicted to violent sports "? Certain it is that some of them are deceiving themselves, certain that some are being deceived. Certainly there is, in the almost child-like urgency and frankness of their efforts to reach us, something more than the mere itch to show off, something that comes very close to practice in perfecting the use of a weapon. *" Madame, I am so young!"* Almost I find in this a note which cannot be the cry of helplessness alone, and then I reproach myself for my suspicious nature. But the devil will out. *" Madame, do you not feel tempted to know how young I really am? Look at this . . ."* and out slips a photograph from the letter. What meaning should one attach to the sending of photographs—if a girl, hair in ringlets and the briefest of skirts; if a boy, in bathing-dress and the briefest of briefs? Well they know, these inspired children, that youth is always a weapon, and one deadlier than ever if it goes hand in hand with beauty.

Fate has decreed, where writing is concerned, that I should be incapable either of holding myself back or of giving instruction. What have I to teach, unless it be

self-doubt, to those who since early youth have become
secretly infatuated by self-love rather than by self-
torture?

O you chorus of cynical child-writers. Children indeed you are, but what pain it is to know you cynical
already, willing to sell yourselves to anyone who offers
you leisure enough, bread enough, warmth enough, even
solicitude enough—objects of barter all—just as it is
difficult not to give you another thought! The whole
problem seems solved for me when I hold to my vow
never to listen to the echo which prolongs certain phrases:
*"Madame, I am fifteen. All my life the imperative urge
to write . . .".* From the brown paper parcel tied with
string and containing sheets already crumpled and faded
from having tried their luck elsewhere, there erupts,
flutters, cascades—I cannot stop it—such an intoxicating
odour of lies, heady despair, bumptious arrogance,
craftily selected truth—an odour, did I say? No, a
menace!

"It seems a pity to eat them," said Marcelle Blot.

"You're not compelled to, Marcelle."

All among my collection of paper-weights, tight-stuffed
with curlicues, burnt sugar twists, flowers and small in-
sects, Marcelle arranged her round, impeccably red
tomatoes, with never a crease or a rib on them, the last
tomatoes from her Saint-Cloud garden, and with a sigh
murmured "Yes, it is compulsory. Because they are
good."

There is about la Grande Marcelle, friend of artists—
and my friend—a faint but pungent smell of tarragon,

chervil and parsley which she had arranged into a bunch
for me round a centrepiece of celery, white as ivory, and
sprigs of purple-flowering thyme. Whatever emerges
from her hands always has a suggestion of the skills of
weaver, braider, florist, and decorator. She dictates the
fashion in women's hats. And then, of a sudden, she
refuses to make any more hats. Because of the hats? No,
because of the women. She retires to Saint-Cloud, and
goes into retreat. She is so essentially unsociable! Yet it
was none other but she who invented the art of delicately
plaiting reeds and raffia into the shape of leaves and
making belts and sandals of them. I have seen her con-
trive a bridal wreath by imaginatively stringing white
pearls of mistletoe berries on the spikes of a branch of
thorns. She arrived from Saint-Cloud to pay me a visit,
graced with the tricolour of a healthy peasant woman,
blue eyes, white teeth, red cheeks.

"So you're not working at the moment, Marcelle?"

"Oh yes I am," she said. "I've constructed something
of such beauty that I waste all my time in admiring it. In
my garden I have four large privet bushes. I'm overrun
with privets, as it happens, and since I could see no future
for them as privet bushes, I wanted to be rid of them.
I've often wondered how they could best be improved,
and now I know. I hollowed out with the clippers the
entire centre of each clump, taking care to leave quite a
thick outer covering, and I removed every leaf from these
branches. Those I had snipped off I interwove in and
out of the ones I had left, till they made a basket, or
rather a cage—the sort of work I am good at—making
the most of a few little apertures here and there in the
close-knit weave. Through these I fitted transverse canes

across the inside, some to serve as perches and others on which to hang food and drink pans. Do you see the idea of my out-of-door cages? I have strengthened the weave on the side of the prevailing wind, and made it thicker still over the top, woven in the shape of a dome."

"And what do the birds say to that, Marcelle?"

She raised her hands in admiration. "The birds? They have talked so much about it that they've got practically nothing more to say. I'd hardly finished the first cage before they knew what it was for. If you could have heard the commotion among them! And their committee meetings, and the contradictory views expressed! I spend my time with them. I've seen three kinds of tit, bullfinches, chaffinches, and others I don't know the name of. My cat laughs behind his paw at me. He must be thinking I don't know the first thing about making a trap. The fact is . . ."

"But what about the birds themselves? Haven't they thought it might be a trap?"

Marcelle's azure blue eyes quizzed me for an instant. "No," she said. "They know who I am. They're already popping in and out through the small windows. The chaffinch goes in with its head down, cramped up like a parakeet. And just imagine, the others fly in and out at full tilt, the very opposite of birds who dislike being caged. It's overwhelming. They tell me that they'll be fighting for possession of my cages when spring comes round."

Marcelle thoughtfully closed down the lid of the basket in which she had brought me the latest adornments of her kitchen garden, before saying with a note of determination in her voice, "So much the worse, in that case. From now on I shall have to invent something to stop them fighting."

She tied her foulard under her chin and made to leave the room, but I called her back.

"Marcelle, Marcelle! Haven't you brought me back my little black velvet hat?"

She poked her beautiful rustic face round the half-open door.

"Did you ever! No, I have not! I've not had the time. My clients the privets were more pressed for time than you! For you hardly ever go out, and they sleep out of doors every night."

IX *Grasse, 1948*

O<small>N</small> each successive day following the appearance of the first fully ripened fig of the second crop, you can count on any number up to a dozen "secondary figs" being ripe and ready to fall into your hand, soft, with inflexed necks, bearing the pheasant's eye mark at their base and on their sides the parallel stripes that crackle their tender skins of mauve and grey. For the first few days you'll not be able to eat your fill. There's little to be said for your appetite if you can't polish off six, ten, or even a dozen figs with the chill of night still upon them; they readily split apart and are as red inside as a pomegranate. They are not as yet runny with their full measure of honey-sweet stickiness, and are so much the easier to put in the mouth.

But the figs multiply with the rapidly increasing rate of maturity. Before the week is out the huge fig tree, the young tree further down, and the contorted tree will all be overwhelmed with ripe fruit, pendent from the neck like the stocking nests of the Haitian cacique bird. There is no end to them. Every single one deserves to be picked and placed on a wicker tray. Time is of the essence, for by now it is easy to see that in their turn the grapes are insistent on being cut, that the tomatoes have reached the peak of their red lacquer lavishness, and all that remain on the peach trees are the fluffy little pellets destined to become the hard ammunition for children to pelt each other with.

After which the trees will bear no further crop but apples, in abundance down in the hollow of the valleys round Grasse and in the orchards of Solliés-Pont. Here and there one of the splendid expatriate Normandy pippins falls into the torrent bed of the Gapeau and bobs along to the astonishment of its now diminished stream.

I might very well have believed the factory for the slow processing of floral essences to be sound asleep within its extensive gardens, had not my arrival coincided with that of a dray drawn by a stout-limbed percheron and loaded with lengthy thick-wicker baskets, scrupulously veiled with heavy cloth. Nine hundred kilos of jasmine blossom were discharged from this rustic equipage. My wheelchair became firmly stuck in their way.

Only four hours previously had they left the fields and they were still perfectly fresh. They were on their way to be consumed and they drew me along in their wake. An atmosphere that could have been cut with a knife existed beneath the ventilated ceilings, yet parted slowly before the silent footfall of the men employed in the service of perfume.

Nine hundred kilos of jasmine blossom lay in a still white litter where they had been summarily dumped on the polished flagstone floor, not far distant from another bed, of withering tube-roses that breathed out the odour of mortal decay yet still retained their flesh-coloured pallor. From these inestimable stacks arose an aura of consenting torpor, almost the desire to be quit of life; there I willingly would have remained, physically, mentally, optimistically exhausted, under the watchful eye of a young lady who had devoted her energies that morning to pushing my wheel-chair. She was a delicious child and I nicknamed her my little fairy horse. When I enquired in some trepidation whether I were not too heavy, she tossed her head up and down in a negative response: nothing is too heavy for a little fairy horse.

The factory owner wished to guide me to the successive fates that awaited in sealed vats the spoils garnered from the various harvests of Grasse: no eye would ever look upon them again as flowers.

The integrity of an industry such as his is an unrivalled marvel. From jasmine is extracted the scent of jasmine, and from iris bulbs the scent of iris. " If you were staying a little longer at Grasse," Maurice Maubert said to me, " I would show you the huge multicoloured mattresses of freshly picked carnations that embalm the air with essence of cloves."

When, on taking my leave of him, I asked at what stage in the proceedings, by what stress of cunning, the scent of jasmine reappeared in the extract of jasmine, he slipped into my hands a packet of that compound known as " *le concret* ", resembling a cake of dark, sticky chocolate, thanks to which, though I had barely touched it, I not long after established the fact that boiled eggs smell of jasmine, that fish salad tastes of jasmine, that baked aubergine and crème caramel follow suit. The man responsible for such an excess of perfumed delights offered no excuse for it, quite the contrary: he filled my cup with hot coffee vaguely enraptured by jasmine, saying "What better proof could I have given you that this concentrated essence of jasmine is irrepressible?"

Toward six in the evening the scent of jasmine begins to bar the roads as effectively as a rope stretched taut across them. All night long and until first light the flowers will make their invisible presence increasingly, potent. All the same, as we pass by on nights the blue of wood ash in the moon's absence we can distinguish the little starry blossoms, white against the dark foliage. Between dawn and sunrise there is time enough for a picking, with nimble fingers that pluck only the corollas and leave behind the tiny sepals. The jasmine bushes are trussed into loose sheaves, both to facilitate the picking and to prevent the flowers from coming into contact with the light soil in which tuberose and sweet onions flourish side by side, and also to spare them the weight of so much as an ant, a grain of sand, or a ladybird!

On evenings when a heat haze reminds us that August is nearing its end, my crippled condition earns me a run in the car. The region round Grasse—which has no summer rainfall—secretes a wealth of subterranean streams. Gushing springs abound, the smallest *mas* has its miniature cascade; each village is supplied with a constant flow of water from the three all but ice-cold jets of a full-bodied stone urn in the *placette*, and often enough this water is beaded with tiny bubbles; at all costs I have to borrow a cup, or drink from the pitcher attached to the fountain-head, as I was wont to do in the past when travelling through Aix-en-Provence. A spring is an eternal miracle.

A property up for sale, where the carriage ways are open to certain visitors, is a babble of bubbling brooks, a simmering of freshets in the shade; with a flourish of crystalline muscles, a solid arm of water gushes up from a gash in the ground. On the tenantless terrace, in the area surrounding a single-pedestalled fountain, time, moisture, birds and winged seeds between them have contributed to the formation of a vast vegetal sponge, where each blade sheds its pearly tear, as at the ancient fountain at Salon.

Whether they break surface or remain beneath it, the waters of Grasse, in the unbroken silence of the pure night air, create an elusive mist in which the jasmine fragrance is entangled and held captive. Nothing stirs before the peep of dawn. As the last stars fade from the heavens and a reddish brown bar rises along the horizon, we are but three—my dearest friend, a striped cat and myself—who infringe the laws of sleep, perched on the heights above the gradation of cultivated terraces. Before ten in the morning there will not be a breath of air to ruffle the leaves of the crinkled, misshapen mulberry, or those of the young plane trees. It was the same at Saint-Tropez, where we used to wait under the huddled wistaria for the moment when the wind from the west and the sun, in conjugation, awoke the sea, the cicadas, the morning glory, and the purslane of four differing colours. In those days, with the confidence of my fifty years, I would stir the sleeping waters to frighten the shy reptilia by dipping my foot in the pools, pick the mauve statice in the salty marsh and at that incomparable hour I would be saddened by the thought that after the first bathe I should have to retire within my shuttered house and work at *Break of Day*. I no longer possess that house, and it is a far hark back to my fiftieth birthday. What is left to me is my avidity. Of all my forces it alone has not humbled itself to time.

I am shown none but the most beautiful things. The kind attentions of my friends, never entirely devoid of humour, ensure that I am taken out for a drive of fifteen miles or so along the whole length of the Croisette, at the very time when among the concourse of bathers the nude figures of a man and a woman are on the point of clambering out of the water on to a float, at the precise moment when one man among a host of others in search of refreshment is staking his claim for a place at the pedestal table for himself and his fruit juice, where one bare back may be heard saying to the bare back beside it in a tone of defiance " But I tell you I've gone a far darker colour than you ". I find the spectacle so strange that I insist, as at a merry-go-round, on having another turn.

Out at sea a boat is towing its pair of water-skis, for all the world like a silvery insect at the end of a line. In their coupled state, and lent enchantment by the distance, their pairing is the only one down here that evokes the idea of love. As for the rest . . . I do not believe I have ever seen a crowd less concerned with love, or so stripped to the buff, as this Cannes Vintage of 1948. They look just about as voluptuous as a keg of sardines, packed in their serried ranks. Let it be said, however, that here the weather is fine, whereas everywhere else it is raining. " Just one turn more? " I am granted it, driving along at a snail's pace between the sea and the dressmakers', the

sea and the jewellers', the sea and the sandal-sellers, the
vendors of brassières and fruit juices, the sea and hotels,
cars, flowerstalls, sun-bathers and walnut-stained women.
One yellow hotel has exceeded all reasonable proportions,
making a mock of architectural harmony. An orchestra
strives to make its feeble strains audible in the open air.
I observe women who, in the guise of bathing costumes,
wear creased or uncreased shorts of poor quality flowered
fabrics and gorgerins like the hollows of one's hands.
Such is their promenading attire of an afternoon; the hem
above the thighs greasy and dirtied by oil. The men, in
the security of a brief and highly revealing slip, give a
far better account of themselves. No matter, there are
far too many of them, men and women alike. " Would
you care to take another turn? "—" No thanks! " I find it
hard to tell whether all this varied display of human
flesh is turning me into a vegetarian, or whether I am
shockingly jealous of those who apparently derive pleasure
from their own agility, the briny, and going naked. I
go back gladly to the slopes of Grasse, though this means
that I must be parted from the sea. It lies beyond the line
of little hills—over there, look!—between those two little
breasts rising from this land that breathes so easily. It's
not so very far away; you'd almost think that by standing
on tiptoe . . . Let us resign ourselves: the sea is not
visible from here. You won't console me by referring
jokingly to the Mediterranean as being hardly worth
calling a sea. There is little doubt, when the mood is on
it, this sea knows only too well how to bring havoc to the
Côte d'Azur.

When at Hyères, though from quite a distance, we
could see its hard lapis blue and its wind-rows of sand.

From where we are now I am taken sometimes in the morning to La Garoupe and dumped down there on the wave-splashed spit of the shore. Below the balustrade the foaming sea joins in the frolics of the naked children; to my now useless feet the feel of the sand is sometimes cool, sometimes warm. At Antibes the evening before last, all along the sea-wall where I was being promenaded in my chair, I saw the sea far better for it being a moonlit night, and for the fact that my turning-point happened to be at the spot where a restaurateur of genius, by placing his tables exactly in the centre of the arc formed by the rampart, has provided his summer clients with an ideal view. On one side are the port and quayside, on the other, in due course and when their hour has struck, appear the light of the moon, the flares of the fishing smacks, and the phosphorescent back of a breaking wave. That night we all felt that nothing could go wrong and everything we could wish for was ours. The patron, brown as a berry and dressed in white tight-fitting clothes from collar to espadrilles, was wreathed in smiles as he came and went with silent tread, chatting freely in anticipation of a long July night devoted to good food and drink.

Between our tables in the foreground and the distant backcloth there passed, some stopping and others not, a succession of those disconcerting touring cars that are to be seen eating up the miles on all roads, noiseless as often as not, yet whose very discretion renders them the more dangerous since, gleaming from the final authoritative flick of the polisher, they seem to rise from an oil-bath only to plunge back into it the very next moment.

The white-clad proprieter felt no apprehension as he watched them approach. He had the knack of applying an

American, Venezuelan, Scandinavian, or Swiss name to
every dress and every face behind its tanned mask that
drew up in front of his premises. Sure of himself, certain
of his minions keenly employed in cooking and gossiping
in the recesses of his kingdom, he would disappear only
to reappear in a twinkling, arms laden, to set before his
guests from Chile or Colombia a long dish of raw
vegetables, white fish piled high, a firm-fleshed *rascasse*,
and, the pride of the evening, a luscious langouste ready
dressed in its rose red carapace.

Few and far between, along the Côte, are the wayside
inns constrained—like the chronometer at Marseilles
which struck the hour for you every forty-five minutes—
to 'fit' their season into two-and-a-half months and to
keep alive their fame and fortune within that limit of
time. The finical tourist—certain of that ilk do still exist
—known to the natives of Provence as *l'estrangier,* can
tot them up on the fingers of one hand. He makes a bee-
line for them, and emerges properly stung. Yet he returns
to them again and again. He is a devotee of the mysteries
of the French cuisine, for all that he may well ruin his
palate by preliminary libations of alcohol. I watched him
at work the other evening in one of those enchanting
spots to be found in the Midi where everything in the
garden is lovely: trees properly tended, plants and shrubs
well watered, maidservants with plump rounded arms
which, the Lord be praised, are kept too busy ever to
grow thin, where mint and basil vie with lemon-scented
verbena in an atmosphere already fragrant with rose-
geranium, suggestive of Morocco.

By half past nine, my four table-companions and I were
feeling pleasantly replete after dining off small red-fleshed

melons, white-fleshed fish, *courges gratinées*, peaches, our
glasses still holding the glint of a young wine—how
difficult nowadays to come by this *tendron du pays*!—
when our eyes were arrested by the arrival of the invaders,
people who never think of dining before ten and who
must have a drink before they eat.

It was up to the hard-working staff to satisfy their every
whim. Into the hands of each was put an identical, heavily
moulded glass embossed with tortuous scrolls, over which
passed a multicoloured cloud-burst of pastis, cocktails,
and champagne. In a twinkling the bright fire of the
drinks was dimmed by the clink of cubic bonbons of
ice.

Showing a certain reluctance to be seated, one or two
clinging couples remained on their feet and began to go
through the vague motions of a dance. Yelping females
intrigued in particular for the embrace of an American
film-star, a man of dubious age, long since gone to seed
and slap-happy in his cups.

Another time, and in another place, I came to a halt
beside an inn that lay just off a main road and sparkled
like an elongated island edged with lights and flowers
behind its fringe of parked cars. Enthroned in state at the
entrance sat she whose presence ensured the prosperity
of the house, *la patronne,* its organiser and its guarantor.
Vast in bulk, she made no bones about it, knowing full
well that in her noble and strenuous calling there is no
authority without fulness of figure. Her impartial smile
provoked no jealousies, yet behind it lurked a hint of
irony. Her speech was concise, clipped, with a detectable
disdain: her " Fish? Meat? Both? ", a typical example.
" What have you got in the way of meat? " asked an

impertinent fellow, assuming, as he hoped, something of the air of an habitué. Sizing him up, she administered a single word snub: "All." The whipper-snapper, disappointed, shifted his ground. "I'd rather have fish. What fish have you got?" "All," the good lady repeated. How my heart warmed to her, how infinitely superior she was to the man who was trying to find something "difficult" on her menu! He chose *truite au bleu* followed by a *ris de veau*. The lady of the house, merciful after her fashion, saw to it that a touch of authentic thick cream was added to the sauce of the sweetbreads. Not but what, the meddlesome diner was not deterred from taking a squint to his right at my piping hot, velvety fish soup, and to his left at a fourfold crêpe, oozing with a bubbly cheese fondant, a speciality of the house.

There is a time and a place for everything. Here we are not assailed by any such twinge of conscience as, in Paris, may reduce us to reprobates when faced by a display of exorbitantly priced delicacies, for here we are proffered in profusion, by hands rich in cunning and traditional skills, the fruits, fish and game of Provence, brought in direct from the kitchen garden or still alive from the farmyard, landed from the sea or from fresh water tanks, or even poached from the neighbouring pine tracts. Heavens! how readily we revert to a state of savage euphoria, eager to set off in pursuit of the black pig in the forests of Tahiti as to sample that imaginary dish which in my part of the country both symbolises and ridicules the extreme of luxury, the dish known as "*fersues de caquesiau*", or, in plain words, "midges' livers". We fly from one extreme to the other: either the shell-fish bristling with legs and claws and coral-trimmings, or else a snack by the road side, a *casse croute marseillais,* soaked in good oil and garlic.

We have only to transplant ourselves, by a turn of the wheel over the dial of France, and we are no longer recognisable, so easily do we become amenable to nature's bounty. Beneath the fig-tree, under the sky-blue plumbago, let yourself go and take your ease in the midst of pimento, sea-urchin, and a well-stocked salad-bowl, with *loup-de-mer* at a thousand francs each and out-of-season game *sur canapé,* let yourself go, openly and in the sight of all! Nothing that we enjoy eating need cause us shame. Nothing is too beautiful or too good to put the finishing touch—just once in a while, what say you?—to the natural lavishness that surrounds us, even though we have to be ready to renounce it all once the time comes for returning to the long, dietary discomfort that has for so long been our portion for three out of the four seasons.

There is always the return journey to be made. We have to leave that which we love and deserves our love, that which touches our heart no less than that which makes us laugh, as for instance the basset hound who could work up an appetite only to the sound and fury of his own pretended ferociousness; no longer can we look forward to a pattering of feet and a morning visit, no longer listen to the prattle of the diminutive artiste who, at the age of eight, displayed both on stage and screen the skill and aplomb of an old stager.

The troublesome question of my return to Paris became the subject of a friendly discussion in my presence. " No, not by train. Anything rather than the train for her. The heat! The car's out of the question.—Why so?—Takes too long. Not comfortable enough.—Right. Then it means by air.—Oh, I don't much like the thought of her going by air . . . —But what, after all, would she like best?—She's not said anything."

She's not said a word. She's not heard, she was reading. She was trying not to laugh. My dearest friend glanced in my direction—what had I got to say? He weighed me up. How best pack an object that one moment agrees to everything, and the next reacts in the strongest possible terms! Where can a basket be found to take this great cat on a journey a thousand miles long? But the cat made up its own mind, and the object gave herself the pleasure of cutting short the debate and choosing to go by air. It is pleasant on occasion to assume the prerogative of a foreman of the jury and decide the issue by a casting vote.

My wheel-chair out on the tarmac, then the hot air bath while waiting for the take-off, the frail of newspapers, a pinch of absorbent cotton-wool to caulk the ears, the neat little lunch-basket and the flagon of wine, all of them prime necessities when travelling Air-France, for I become bored in a plane. Nothing up there is to my liking except the speed. " See, we still have a strip of the sea to cross! Do look, that ribbon of a road down there, surely that's the very route we took last week! " A fig for the route, and for the unexpected cloud we pierce straight through as though it were a cocoon!

I confess my inaptitude. Once before, on the Toulouse-Fez-Toulouse circuit, I realised that riding on high is not for me. My flights of fancy do not rise above ground level. " Look down there, do you know that we are passing right over your native heath? " And do you believe, companion mine, that I am going to recognise my native heath in this flying mist with its criss-crossing roads, its chequerboard of fields cloven by a streak of water you tell me is the Yonne? Not a hope! One thing is certain. Even if I do happen to draw my inspiration from the malicious sense of fun that lies at the ever impenitent heart of septuagenarians, even if I do have to reckon with my impotence and at the same time with the spirit of curiosity engendered by it, I never wish to travel by air again unless it is a question of saving precious hours. Whilst I am being borne along by it I forget the aircraft, for it possesses the magic power of eliminating distances. Thus all we have contact with is the point of departure and the distant goal which looms up out of nowhere before our eyes. My flights of fancy remain on ground level. But you, winged monster, you withhold them from me, for you alone can make the descent! It is the descent and not the sudden uprush into the wilderness of clouds that I find enchanting. Four hours, it takes you but four hours to muster a miniature France beneath your wings, crushing her mountains, obliterating her towns. Finally I achieve the greatest miracle of all: my red and white room, the bed on which I navigate my own course, the stage moonlight of my blue lantern: all that, and I did not know it, is but four hours from Nice.

Oᴜʀ first meeting—1894 or '95?—took place before lunch at the house of Catulle Mendès. The sun was streaming into the room and at that mid-day hour its light gave a vivid outline to the long silhouetted figure of a slight young woman who was leaning forward under the weight of the load she was carrying; this turned out to be a fine, heavy child of between eighteen months and two years old. Fair as summer, he turned to look at me with his grave dark eyes, inherited from his mother.

This splendid child, whose birth had all but caused the death of so frail a mother, this child of light himself died of meningitis before he was three, after battling against death with a strength already far beyond his years. There are few of us left now who remember his short life. And I believe that Moreno—the lovely, austere name chosen by Marguerite Moreno—hardly ever spoke of him except to those of her own age who, like myself, had caught a glimpse of this son of too early promise during his brief existence.

In the home of Catulle Mendès I failed to pay proper attention either to the excellent coffee prepared with his own hands, or to the anti-Semitic couplet, always to hand, which enhanced his reputation as a wit. I had neither eyes nor ears for anything but the tall young woman.

Her own wit, the easy and sparkling delivery of her words, the timbre of her voice which rejoiced the ear of the listener, the unredeemed pallor of her complexion, a head of magnificent chestnut hair with here and there a glint of gold! I can still see the warm look in her unwavering, lively eyes that scorned any coquettish appeal. Everything about her humiliated and enchanted the exiled country lass that I was at the time. From the first moment of this encounter I admired and adored Marguerite Moreno. The astonishing thing is that she returned my affection. We were young enough, having both recently come of age, for our friendship to develop into the sort of schoolgirl crush which young ladies at boarding schools find so intoxicating. Throughout the period that Mendès contributed theatrical notices to *Le Journal*, he would frequently take us both to the critic's box. I squeezed myself in between his crumpled shirt-front and Moreno's lovely swanlike neck. One night he took us to a music hall.

"You're going to see the strangest little creature," Marguerite said to me. "Any producer worth his salt ought to grab hold of her and rescue her from herself and her idiotic songs. Even from her stage-name, which is quite ridiculous. She's gifted with the most attractive ugliness, and she looks as if she invented her own dance numbers."

At that time Polaire was twirling and spinning on the boards of the Scala, like a midge caught in a sunbeam. She had not yet had her auburn hair cut short—auburn, mind you, not black. Her stage costume, the perfectly cut dress of a period "smasher", did credit to the taste and talent of Madame Landolff who, as a costumière, has had no equal. A full, short, nondescript skirt concealed, when not in motion, its embroidered underside ablaze with concentric circles of all the colours of a rainbow. The least twitch made by the midget singer—during the reprise she danced with eyes shut and arms stiff like a woman falling asleep—would unfurl about her, around legs in a froth of black lace, the seven reverberant colours. Her hair, swept up and back and twisted into a clown's topknot, displayed two exquisite ears, which later in her career were hidden by her short hairstyle.

Madame Landolff delighted in designing dresses for her, all of which seemed deserving of a better fate than a music-hall turn. I well remember one of white lace, like rigid spindrift against that brown statuette. I can see another, a miracle of rustling silk resembling paper, in dark and ever-changing shades of green, slashed with a hundred small cuts that opened upon an acid pink foundation during the dance; a mat terra cotta dress closely matching her skin, which appeared to be naked, decked with a few mauve feathers.

"What did I tell you?" said Moreno. "She looks like nobody else. Perhaps she is a wraith after all."

For at that time Moreno herself was unaware whose compelling hand it was that would drag the dancing and singing, rainbow-encircled Polaire away to the legitimate theatre.

I am forever losing only to discover afresh my very earliest memories of Marguerite Moreno, for the lives we both led tended to scatter and then reassemble them. She travelled far and wide, I never stirred. We both got married, became unmarried, married again. She dwelt in the pure regions of poetry, and tried her hand at

imparting higher education to the Argentians; I played in
pantomime at the Apollo and elsewhere. After lengthy
silences, which caused me to fear the worst, an exchange
of letters would put us back where we were, at the heart
of an unbroken friendship. On leaving the Argentine,
she returned to the stage in one of those deplorable plays
by Bataille that were saved only by their cast—Bady,
Yvonne de Bray, Huguenet.

She staged her return at the Vaudeville, in *La Phalène*.
During my pregnancy I used to hoist my burdened
body up to her dressing-room where, of an evening, she
would lavish on me in short flashes the colour, flavour,
adventures and disillusionments of her sojourn in the
Argentine. "Yes, yes, *mon vieux*, the very first night, a
butterfly the size of a vulture, with a luminous nose,
flapped all over my room making as much din as a
threshing-machine! Didn't you hear my cries for help
from here?" She knew how highly I prized a description
depicted in the strongest colours, the delight I took in
the enlargement of the thing described, and we would
"mon vieux" each other like children at a village school.

Today I find it surprising that at the very time when
she attained the full glory of womanhood, when thanks
to the Argentinian climate she returned with healthier
cheeks and a fuller bust (in the title rôle of *The Green
God* she showed off her superb long legs), she should
have dropped her charming and romantic first name. Her
public called her "Moreno". Her friends and ardent
admirers—she always had them in abundance—referred
to her as "Moreno", a dusky name that beautifully
suited her matchless pallor with its suggestive hidalgo
look. When she was acclaimed a star celebrity, when the

vast array of cinema-goers became infatuated with her trenchant yet restrained gift for playing comedy, as a delicate act of gratitude the crowds restored to her her lovely christian name. In all public places it was hurled at her. " Marguerite . . . there's Marguerite! " More intimidated than she wished to let it appear, she would flutter her eyelashes when struck by this flower.

After Marcel Schwob, who was madly in love with her, she was married for a time to Jean Daragon, the actor, on whom a false beard could confer the elegant virility of *The Ironmaster* by Georges Ohnet, or the poetic hirsute-ness of Richepin's *The Tramp*. Ill health kept Daragon out of the First War, and no woman ever excelled Moreno in lightening the protective yoke as she watched over this man of fragile health camouflaged as a bruiser in the pink of condition. So skilful was her gentle raillery that he never detected the anxiety or the pity behind her smiling mask. But she was unable to prevent him from dying even though she took him with her to Nice, where she worked in a hospital for the wounded. If only I had kept every one of the letters she wrote to me at that time!

" I carry on with my duties among my legless ones, who are gay, and my armless ones, who are sad. It doesn't take long before my legless ones are drawing, writing, making small toys, propelling themselves from place to place as best they can, and getting up to every sort of nonsense. Whereas my armless ones grow melancholy: because for a man it must be the greatest humiliation, perhaps the worst of all, never again to be able to undo his own trouser buttons without a helping hand."

For long months of the long war we both remained

faithful to Paris, living as near neighbours. She lived on
the ground floor of a modern house in Rue Jean-de-
Bologne and I in a Swiss chalet in Rue Cortambert. Annie
de Pène had a cottage, with steps running up to it, at the
very end of the countrified Herrent blind-alley. Musidora
had recently done up one of those bachelor establishments,
in a wedge-shaped gore in Rue Decamps, a single room,
with hot water, central heating, and bathroom "with
every convenience", that put to shame anything our
tottering houses in old Passy had to offer. On nights when
the sky was peopled with Zeppelins, she would sleep at
Rue Cortambert on a small iron bed, and do the shopping
and cooking in the day time. I acted as char and did the
washing. We made up a fine female squad! We used to
tie the hand-washed sheets round a stout copper faucet
and wring them out by twisting them tight, while
Marguerite Moreno, a cigarette between her lips, would
sprinkle our domestic chores with the beneficent dew of
news, true or false, anecdotes, and prognostications. Annie
de Pène knew of a certain carriage gateway beneath
which a man from the country sold chickens, tossing them
over to her with an "Up she goes, little lady! Now chuck
me my four francs five sous!"

It was the hardest thing in the world for us to break
up for the night. From those black times dates Moreno's
inspiring influence on Annie de Pène, on her daughter
Germaine Beaumont, and on Musidora. We drank in the
consolation of lovely words, sinuous verse, the distant
scene, all magically evoked. In the shadow of Moreno
followed Jean Daragon, bulky and breathing with
difficulty. My little garden brought forth its usual offerings and, after a watering, exhaled its garden smells. My

daughter was enjoying life in the unravaged Limousin;
the finest Paris peaches cost five sous apiece.

All the members of our phalanstery of the XVIth
arrondissement owed a debt of gratitude to Moreno, for
there she sowed the good seed of laughter, inimitably,
miraculously, the laughter of crises, the nervous, un-
restrained laughter of war-time, self-assertive insolence in
face of looming danger, the cut and thrust of wordplay
as intoxicating as drafts of wine. On windless nights the
belch of the howitzers, each distinct, reached us from the
east. This deep-seated, close-sounding concussion had the
effect of silencing conversation, and was transmitted
through the distorted regions of the air to reach as far
as our deserted but keenly alert quarters. It happened one
night that Moreno, doubtless at a loss for verbal quips,
became engrossed in the rhythm of the cannonade, snapping her fingers and clicking her heels as it rose and fell,
and improvising on the spot a mock-Spanish dance; with
a twist of her hips and a roll of her eyes she restored
laughter to our midst, banishing all thought of danger
by a display of healthy impertinence with the temerity of
a heroine. Pierre Fresnay can surely not have forgotten a
post-war occasion at Marseilles, when we, Marguerite,
he and I, were leaving the theatre about midnight after
playing in *Chéri!* Moreno was brilliant in her improvisa-
tions as she sniffed the aniseed-laden air of the Cannebière
and instructed Fresnay in the joyous adventures of
nomadic life. She left him doubled up with laughter, completely dazzled by her arresting glance and the wide range
of her fanciful imagination.

I can still see the gasping tip of her cigarette that was
hardly ever stubbed out—" Marguerite, you're smoking

too much "—her honest appetite that never boggled at
the foie gras and black pudding of the snack-bars—
"Marguerite, you'll make yourself ill!" Her own special
gifts, and among them I would choose the sudden serious-
ness and fullest over-tone accorded to the measure of the
alexandrine, and the healing magic to charm all creatures,
for I benefited from them for more than fifty years, but
intermittently, alas! One cannot always have the good
fortune to play Léa in *Chéri* when Madame Moreno has
consented to play the part of Charlotte Peloux! In
Brussels, as elsewhere, I learned many a lesson from her
genuinely roving accomplishments. She would watch me
with detachment as I arranged a writing-table, put three
flowers into a vase, or set out on a plate a bunch of fresh
but insipid large grapes. Already up in her room she had
half-unpacked her valise, hung up her scotch cape, and
chucked a packet of cigarettes and the day's paper on the
table. On going into it I would exclaim "Marguerite
Moreno's room, I can tell by the smell of it." For a linger-
ing personal fragrance, to which my keen sense of smell
has always been highly susceptible, denoted her presence.
Nothing whatever to do with body odour, it was not
axillary—"I'm drier than tinder," she was in the habit
of saying—nor did it derive from any perfumed essence
or lotion.

The particular place on her neck below the ear, where
I would give her a kiss of greeting, was embalmed with
the invariable, captivating scent of her skin, as well as
that of tobacco smoke. All you many men who have at
some time or other been violently in love with Marguerite,
you at least can never have failed to note, never have

forgotten the scent exhaled by her glorious, creamy skin, with a hint of amber beneath its white texture!

An hotel bedroom, by no means the best, a valise or two, a book, two volumes of verse, a manuscript, a cape, *the* cape—a reversible tartan—that she would lend to anyone in need of it (it once saved my dearest friend and me from a downpour of hail that lashed our open carriage), from this meagre assortment of props she was capable of creating comic effects by sheer force of will. On the stage, a gold or silver shoe might occasionally peep out from beneath the hem of her skirt; the foot it shod, worthy of the fairest raiment and itself beyond compare, was designed for freedom and, naked, to tread the coolness of flagstones, a foot such as that of M'Barka, the bare-foot dancing-girl of the Pasha of Marrakesh.

When touring the provinces Moreno and I were sometimes able to keep together. Pierre Moreno used to play Patron, the boxing instructor, in *Chéri*. Every now and again he would work off his homesickness by singing songs in his native Gascon dialect, well suited to his delightful tenor voice. All three of us loved Brussels, the gilt of its Grande Place, the busy gaiety of its inhabitants, the beer, the coffee, the buttered slices of tasty Belgian bread; while sitting outside that huge restaurant, you must know it, *Les Trois* . . . whatever it was, we would bathe in the stream of passers-by and enjoy our bohemian idleness to the full.

Moreno did not put aside much money from her earnings at that time. Later on the cinema woke up to the fact that it was worth their while to offer her a fortune. She accepted with disillusioned serenity. She owned certain properties, among them an exceptionally blue " Blue

Spring ", an ancient castle, as well as patrimony and land
more than sufficient to satisfy her needs. Who could have
imagined that the first few months of 1948 would be the
last of her life! According to the demands made on her
by cinema, theatre, and late-night cabaret, she pitched her
tent first in an hotel in the Batignolles district before
moving to one in the Avenue de l'Opéra. Knowing that
I had for some time been unable to stir from my room, she
would conquer any feelings of fatigue, walk a little way
along the Avenue de l'Opéra, take for fun one of the
little passages that honeycomb the Palais Royal, climb up
the flight and a half to where I lay, and appear decked
out in her usual array; cigarette, felt hat pulled down
over one eye, and coat the colour of dusk and rain. Oh,
how grateful I was to her for being always her own true
self, ready to set off again and again, fagged out but
untiring! How I loved her perpetual motion which, truth
to tell, never parted me from her, loved her for her
regularity in writing to me when far away, her zest for
work which seemed to keep her young! I would make
the pretence of putting her through a severe cross-
examination.

"Marguerite, I demand nothing but the truth. Where
have you come from? "

"From Courbevoie. I'm filming."

"What is the film? "

"Less than nothing, as you might suppose. And I had
a matinée at the A.B.C."

"Are you hungry? Thirsty? "

"I had lunch in the taxi. But rest assured, tonight I'll
have a bite of foie gras and champagne. Always supposing I have the time. You see, I have two performances

at the A.B.C. and I've promised to go back to Courbevoie."

"When?"

"In . . . in ten minutes. After that, as you know, I'm giving a poetry reading at Tonton's at midnight."

"How many more nights have you got to put in at Tonton's?"

Her lovely hand flew to my shoulder and, with a gentle look, she stared me straight in the face.

"That, Macolette, is something I never wish to come to an end! Cabaret, as I have come to know, is something unique. Just think of it, I'm in the process of teaching them Verlaine. *They* gulped down Baudelaire like an untried drink. If only you could see them! For the most part, they have come there for the champagne, and the hell of it. I wrung their withers with Hugo and Delavigne all right, that was relatively easy work. But to lead them to the water of Baudelaire and Verlaine! With the slightest encouragement I'll win them over to Mallarmé! There I sit surrounded by their heat and their smell, their knees make room—but not always—for mine, by making a long arm I get a light off one of them, I fish for a cigarette in the cases held out to me. You can picture the scene! You hear them bawling, then watch them gradually grow silent till you feel they are listening. It's like the courts of heaven, with the crowd pressing in upon the speaker."

She lowered her eyes with pride, showing a reserve in which I have many a time found, a purely personal discovery, a look approaching sensuality. Now that she will never again stand beside the divan-bed, never again be the life and soul of Tonton's overheated cabaret, why should I conceal from my reader one trait among a hundred others in my attempted portrait of Marguerite? This lowering of the eyelids, which was her way of breaking in on a phrase, of hiding a part of her thought, was one of the rare movements, lasting but a moment, that to my mind brought to Moreno's broad, austere, pale features a significant flash of sensual pleasure.

After giving a defiant laugh, and making me laugh with her, she asked what time it was, hurriedly drew her coat round her, hurriedly made for the door after bending her tall figure over my raft that I might kiss Marguerite's fragrance, under her ear. But she remembered before leaving the room to point on her own body to the seat of some discomfiture "Bitch of a leg, and now this sciatica!"

Perhaps her object was to prevent me in my half-helpless state from envying her lovely slender feet, still capable of going up and down the staircase of the Palais Royal unaided.

She liked to see me alone, when no one else was there. She liked to see Madame Brisson alone, or one or other of her daughters. She liked to see Jeanne Roze without me, and Pierre Blanchar when no third person was present. More than I could name, and I don't believe I knew them all, were those with whom Marguerite Moreno loved to hobnob tête-à-tête. All of us, without exception, showed ourselves jealous of the moments that she spared for each one of us. What we had to have was Marguerite Moreno between our window and our fire-place, the famous felt hat, for so it became, pulled down over one eye, her well-worn vanity bag, her cigarettes, her untiring voice. I was sorry when she gave up wearing her hair in the style that became so long the hallmark of every rôle she played, the neat well-groomed cut of a man-about-town, exactly fitting the shape of her head. At her wrist jangled a wide-linked gold bracelet. What more can I recollect of her who showed contempt for all outward finery? A ring? Probably. But one's eye rested not on the ring but on the hand, a hand needlessly elongated and exaggerated in its refinement in the portrait that now hangs in the Luxembourg. I can forgive the artist, Granier, in favour of the speaking likeness; there, at its frankest, with every dissembled thought removed, there is the face of Marguerite Moreno between the age of twenty and twenty-five.

She suffered considerably, I believe, and with barely a word of complaint, from the life of the film-studios. It is a cruel life for sensitive minds and bodies, in that it brings face to face beings who were particularly intended never to confront one another—a form of brutality from which life in the wings of a theatre has been up till now exempt. During the hours in the studio when she was not on the set, Marguerite, respected by all, withdrew herself to the best of her ability behind a screen of newspapers, feigning drowsiness or a desire for rest. Her perfect manners, which made it impossible for her to snub or show the least sign of impatience, did not come to her effortlessly, I am convinced. Many were the times when I tried to question her about those working days which began at dawn in an outer suburb, the endless rehearsals during which the player extracts from the part, like pus from a gathering, some short phrase that has to be tested for sound over and over again, until its sterling worth is proved by its ring and practice has made it indiscernibly perfect. I still remain wilfully ignorant of the silver screen and its various techniques, a fact that proves me a person not only of a certain age but, as they say, of another age altogether.

Marguerite would tell me little or nothing in reply; shaking her head, she would gently say "You simply cannot imagine what the life of a film actor or actress is like. Impossible, I tell you. I have accepted it, I have no cause either for reproach or explanation. Macolette, drop the subject."

I have already spoken of her various abodes, of her gift for imposing her personality on them however commonplace they were to start with. It would seem that pure chance guided her choice. Rue Jean-de-Bologne, Rue Saint-Louis-en-l'Ile, Rue Notre-Dame-des-Champs, Boulevard du Montparnasse. But the moment she was in them, they became worthy of her presence. Whether she really cared for them I cannot be sure, it was I who became attached to them. Never shall I forget her kindness to me when she was lodging in Place Pereire, at a time when I stood in great need of moral support and could go for it to none but Marguerite. I would climb her stairs and ring the bell at the half-landing. In her room I remember a rough Spanish chest, a round table, the single place laid on it encroached on by a number of books, the books themselves forced into retreat by a strong cheese, a foie gras or some form of sausage meat, all from the Lot. The sun entered from the right quarter. The plum tart came from the near-by confectioner's. "Help yourself, Macolette.—I'm not hungry.—If you're feeling peckish, help yourself. Food is good for you in the state you're in. Sit down. I'm going to tell you the story of my life and of my miracles."

I wonder who is the present tenant of that low-ceilinged lodging from which has departed, if not the sunbeam, at least the presence that bestowed on it meaning and life! Marguerite Moreno left it as she left all the others, neither on sudden impulse nor from dislike. She particularly liked, I think, her last Paris domicile—I do not count hotels—Boulevard du Montparnasse, within easy distance of the blazing Rotonde, the warm glow of the many-coloured brasseries, the combination of deference and familiarity that escorted and vociferously saluted Marguerite Moreno along the wide sidewalks of the avenue.

Previously she had frequented the grey cement of some sort of new-style barracks, and about 1900—with Marcel Schwob—the period wood-panelling and frigid elegance of a house on the Ile Saint-Louis. The creamy white and narrow bourgeois respectability of Rue d'Argenteuil held no terrors for her. A few months before the end she was cracking up to me the genial good-nature and coun-trified fun of a family pension near the Batignolles. She also cracked them up to Pierre Moreno, who began to worry, came up to town from Touzac and found her in one of those hotels whose secret belongs to Paris and which are never without an antimacassared drawing room or a large, lavishly dismal garden. By dint of per-suasion and authority he succeeded in winning her away from this romantic background and establishing her in more up-to-date comfort. But she complained about it to me and, despite all Pierre Moreno's solicitude, her kindly hosts were not prevented from shedding copious and heart-felt tears at her departure. " I should have liked to stay on there a little longer to please them," she confided to me. "They were so nice." How I adored the occasional weakness of one who gave every outward appearance of being able to measure up to both the dangers of living alone and those of a life à deux with the same unwavering eye.

I had the pleasure of applauding Moreno in *La Folle de Chaillot*. A sharp attack of arthritis made me fear up to the last moment that I should have to stay at home. But I was sustained by the good wishes of my friends and overcame my reluctance. Jouvet gave me his stage box, my dearest friend his arm, and a lady unknown to me her unexpected and providential shoulder, at the very moment when I was about to collapse in the foyer. I attached considerable importance to that evening performance. Before long Paris was to show even more regard and enthusiasm than myself. I found at the Athénée exactly what I had anticipated: virtuosity in the acting, Giraudoux in an ebullient mood, and in myself a certain lack of warmth. I had no great liking for the text. I was therefore not open to criticism when I surrendered myself to the delights of Bérard's décor and to my irrepressible admiration for Jouvet, to whom all must be forgiven in recognition of his inventiveness and tyrannical despotism. Finally I had eyes only—I am coming to the point—for Marguerite Moreno, totally absorbed in creating before our eyes the part of La Folle. Such a store of apparent naturalness, so perfectly simulated a disregard for the audience, the control of a commanding voice in allotting to each salient word in a clever sentence its due share of sonority and rhythm, the audacious sallies of a dolled-up warhorse, in short the orchestration of the rôle by an incomparable artiste had in it the power to overwhelm us, and overwhelm us it did.

From the shadows of the stage-box I subjected Marguerite as indiscreetly as you please to the full force of my faculties, with an eye as critical as that of a dresser or stage manager.

I was soon reassured. Under the coating of black and white chalk, beneath the tinsel frippery of her clothes, a great artiste was observing us, a keen-eared musician was profiting by our silence just as much as by our applause. Once my fears were allayed, my pride assuaged, I was able that evening—it was, I think, the fifth performance —to forecast a long and triumphant run for Moreno, and prosperity for the Athénée.

That I might taste and enjoy to the full one dazzling pleasure only, I denied myself for once all interest in the writing, and I would not have exchanged my lack of warmth on that evening for no matter what brand of enthusiasm.

Moreno's inspiration in her part did not begin to wane till after several hundred performances. I have never much cared for the way the public have of judging a stage performance as they would a track event, and applying the term "exhausting" to the eighteen hundred lines or so that devolve upon La Folle. Passing serenely through both moments of anxiety and ovation, Moreno pursued her triumphant way once and often twice a day at the Athénée, yet still found time to visit me.

" But you don't even look tired! " I said in admiration.

" I am tired all the same," she said. " All those stairs to climb up and down! The dryness in the air that's so harmful to one's throat, the lengthy periods of standing about on the set . . ."

I interrupted her with a gesture she understood.

"Oh yes, I see, the exacting nature of my part! Macolette, bear in mind that if I don't look tired it's because I'm not very tired. What I have to do comes quite easily to me. La Folle is a very long part, an eccentric part requiring no great subtlety. It carries no mysterious psychological overtones, so it doesn't take a lot out of me. Would you like to know what I really think? No one has a better claim than you to be privy to it. It's my idea that anybody could play the part, no matter who. Only . . ."

She broke off to open her bag and go through the ritual of muttering: "My key—I've lost my key! Oh no, there it is! I've left my money on the mantelpiece. . . . And now what have I done with Pierre's letter!"

"Only," she resumed, "nobody realises it. On reflection, I think it would be best if nobody but us two ever did know it."

And now here I am giving it away, I, the faithless trustee of this strange confession that bears the stamp of excessive modesty and mystery-weaving fantasy, crying it aloud; but it no longer carries its confidential tone, its accompanying look. She left it with me one day just as she was making off under the wing of her felt hat—chestnut was it, or beige that day, or possibly aubergine!

I did not go a second time to hear *La Folle de Chaillot*. Moreno used to come occasionally to give me news of it, never failing to laugh at herself.

"Still going from strength to strength, Marguerite?"

"Still going strong. Between performances they bring along children for me to bless."

There would follow some anecdote or other that took her back, that took us both back into her past. Any resemblance she might have had to her mother—whose malevolent, well-preserved good looks I remember—assumed on her own lips the mordant quality of an inspired replica. When made up as an elderly woman in a comic film, she would suddenly remind me of her mother (as in *Les Jeux sont faits*) so forcibly, so majestically, as to be disconcerting. When she played the White Ghost in *La dernière Nuit de Don Juan*, one saw for the last time, between the folds of her tightly drawn veil, one saw the dazzle of beauty fall on features that for so long had disdained it.

I keep on looking all about me for Marguerite Moreno. While she was alive we could do without each other for long periods at a time. A telephone call or an exchange of letters would give me back across the space that separated us the tone of her voice and all its clarity. My colleagues, her friends and admirers have given me a bitter-sweet pleasure by printing in the papers an ever increasing number of likenesses hitherto unknown to me. I have been provided with all save her living presence.

Shortly before her death she had invited a grand-niece to stay with her. She had been incapable of hiding her astonishment, her deep feelings, at the sight of a human flower full of health and intelligence. This I deduce from her last letters, in which I find an affectionate constraint, a feeling of watchful pride, even to the extent of discovering something quite new to her, the freedom to welcome by name the idea of the future, at the suggestion

of a radiantly beautiful child. Yet in all this persisted a
reticence, blurred by a sort of timidity in speaking of the
future, of a state of permanency, in admitting the possibility of her life easing off as a result. Only after hesitation would she have sacrificed the poetic and wandering
use to which she had put the autumn of her days.
Her letters, which are the letters of an artist expert in
the choice of words, might cherish the idea of further
spiritual adventures, but surely, for her, the most en-
thralling project would have been to renounce the adven-
turous! A little prudence on her part, a less glacial March,
and Marguerite Moreno would still be with us. Or else,
some hundred miles from here, she might have preferred
to be free of the life-long fetters of her art in the enjoyment of her own wondrous blue spring, her vines and
cultivated lands, and enhanced family circle! "This
year," she wrote to me, "you are going to find a new
creature when you come to stay with me, so much has
everything changed since your first visit! This year you
are at last coming to live in my lovely countryside . . ."

At this point, I don't doubt, she paused in her writing
to let her eyes linger on her estate, on the jewelled blues
that the darting black-backed fish set flashing in her
spring waters, to let her ears listen for the cry of a very
small child. Yet this time, too, she did not dare to write
"home" in place of "countryside".

XI

H YSSOP, my dear Sir, it must be hyssop, this already
shrivelled twig that still keeps its clinging scent and
is almost as delicate as snow crystals. But I do not guarantee this. Just because Mermod's, the Swiss publishing
firm, have issued a little book of mine, in which I speak
of a few plants in the most familiar terms either informa-
tively or to their detriment, it hardly deserves to be compared by you to *La Botanique des Dames*, an excellent
work where you will see pictures of elegant ladies of the
manor hunting for mushrooms in patent leather dancing-
shoes and full flying flounces, and butterflies dying in
agony under white-gloved fingers!

Yes, I incline to the view that it is hyssop. Starting from
pure camphor, its scent runs the whole gamut of two or
three chaste perfumes suggestive of capsicum, such as
lavender and rosemary, before it ends up as—why, in
heaven's name!—as hyssop. *Hysopo et mundabor!* Would
you like me to sing to you over the telephone a good part
of the mass in latin? I could. You would never believe
your ears, my dear Sir with the good sense not to give
your name, so you must take my word for it, that the little
sweet-smelling herb is hyssop: myself, I take it for one
of those presents that fly out from a letter, roll out of a

cabbage leaf or pill-box, in other words, one at which I should never dream of turning up my nose.

Before yours came today I had already received, from H. E. Brahim el Glaoui, a bottle from Marrakesh filled with some grey antimony, spangled and delicate, which goes by the name of kohl, koheul, or mokoheul—I cannot be sure which is the right name for it. What does the spelling matter, now that I am well supplied with cosmetic which can act as a surgical dressing, which prevents the eyes from reddening, allows one to face up to a strong light, sun or electric, and dust-laden air into the bargain: in short, the antimony they use throughout the orient to slip in between the eyelids of newborn babes!

For a great many years I religiously went to buy my koheul at Bichara's, "Syrian Perfumer", from a thin, slight, swart man whose handshake was always so dry and so gentle. He supplied all the very latest novelties, from clay for washing the hair to cakes of soap the shape of small cylinders that looked good enough to eat. I recollect that he never failed to touch wood when asking after my baby daughter, to protect her from the powers of evil. He spoke very low, in a tired voice, and coughed a discreet cough, which was to land him, discreetly enough, in the grave! A man with an aura of physical distinction about him, which gave his place of business an air of enchanted alchemy. He left a daughter who wrote poetry.

I am indebted to a lady from Oran, the wife of General C.—she had married a man of my father's year in the army, a young and dashing captain—for my daily habit of using antimony. A converted Jewess, the general's lady instructed me in many a nicety practised by inmates of the harem, among them the regular use of kohl. In her widowhood, she still affected some peculiarly African forms of adornment, such as hair-curlers of leather, ropes of blue pearls or necklaces of gazelle-droppings, and other magical fetishes, despite all of which she never missed going to mass on a Sunday. In Paris, where I once stayed with her for three weeks, I soon developed a liking for couscous and the plump sweetmeats of Oran.

All the same, I never dared to ask Sido, my mother, for leave to pay a second visit to Paris, or to tell her how one morning there I had happened upon the general's wife while she was busy supervising the household chores of a former batman turned house-boy. Perched high on a double ladder and wearing a blue apron, the lad was engaged in wiping the panes of a fan-light, to the accompaniment of a stream of advice from his Oranese mistress positioned at the foot of the ladder. "You short-arsed little runt," she cursed him roundly, "I can see from here the streaks and blurs you've left on the glass! What you want is a touch of encouragement, eh!" And with that she wantonly seized hold of him by the rump in so tight a grip that he whinnied with surprise and delight. Then he leapt down off the ladder and returned the compliment.

I was then at that uncompromising age when one denies to persons of advanced years the right to indulge in amorous love, when one takes exception to the slightest gesture which may give rise to love and disapproves most thoroughly should it find expression in unseemly high jinks. Far more than the playful prank played by Madame la Générale, it was the man's answering cackle that sent me indignantly back to the room I had just left. I was fifteen! The very age when one quivers with scandalised horror at the salacious behaviour of one's elders. At fifteen, love is on the brink of tears for a yes, for a no: it sees nothing to be amused at in the pinching of buttocks.

Like most dogs with big rounded heads—bull-dogs, bull-terriers, little Brabançon terriers, and boxers—her memory was acute. My elder brother's boxer bitch *knew* several songs, and Souci, my own French bull-dog bitch, an exceptionally large number of words: she was so quick in picking them up that for my own amusement I would give her a few faulty pronunciations. She adored fruit, with a marked preference for ripe raspberries and grapes, and to these, but solely for her own benefit, I gave the names of "raspbeeries" and "gripes". Sometimes, when this ritual had slipped my memory, I would say to her "Would you like a raspberry, or a grape?", and she would then give me a puzzled look and say nothing. I would then correct myself: "A nice little raspbeery? A gripe?", upon which Souci took heart at once and bounced forward full of overjoyed acquiescence. So it was until the day when she made the discovery that not only the vines but the raspberry canes as well bore their fruit within the reach of a full grown bull-dog; thereafter she dispensed with my help and my mispronounced vowels, and went out at seven in the morning to breakfast off raspbeeries and gripes.

I had bought her at the Tuileries Dog Show, where she had won First Prize for French bull-dogs, Class "7 kilos and under", and I had paid nine thousand francs for her. Her brother, sold for his weight in gold, went off to

America. This transaction made such a hole in my pocket that I had to forego my new tailor-made costume and afternoon "ensemble" in order to enrich Souci's wardrobe with a scarlet morocco-leather harness. It is possible that when we went out together the threadbare state of my right elbow and my felt hat (the one the Comtesse de Noailles called my "old huntsman's cap") between them gave me a rather moth-eaten look, but the bitch attracted every eye. In all our eleven years together, Souci and I never encountered a similar couple where so much envious admiration was bestowed on the bull-dog.

For some little time before Souci's day, three of us were to be seen taking our constitutional in the Bois de Boulogne: Belle Aude, a sheep dog from the Beauce, on her high black-and-flame-coloured paws, myself on my bicycle, and Pati, the miniature terrier from Brabant, tucked away in a strawberry basket tied on to my handlebars. On reaching the less frequented rides, I would put the impetuous little lady from Brabant down on the ground, where she invariably did her best to outpace the huge shepherdess from the Beauce. Both came to heel only when the weight and effect of my words of command were fully appreciated because given in the vernacular.

More than one passer-by would remain stationary with surprise for a good minute, on observing that the two bitches were able to distinguish between their right and their left without the slightest hesitation, and of taking up their position on the nearside of my machine.

The Last Cat knew the melody of one song only, a pleasing American number, delightfully sung by the Sophomores, or by the Revellers. Sometimes, when she was sleeping the venerable sleep of cats I would put on the familiar record. She did not always completely wake up, but as she lay dozing a smile of dreamy connivance would blossom on her enchanting lips: "Yes, yes, I hear it. Don't wake me up altogether." I think the title of her song was "Blue Heaven". You may be sure that if and when I buy another gramophone, I intend to buy that record as well.

If ever I cease to sing the praises of the Last Cat, it will be when I no longer have anything to say about anything. Perhaps that day is not far off; but since it has not yet arrived, and since I have been able to tell only of what I know, I still have a word or two to say on this subject and on that, to prevent myself from falling back on my old loves: not that these bring a blush to my cheeks, or that I have any wish to run them down, but simply because there are more than enough of them. I have no longer any desire to look at myself in the mirror of the past with my hair in the style of a gentleman about town or, for that matter, adorned with a wreath of pompom roses.

The vogue for the chestnut poodle is clearly nearing its end, and that of the black cocker spaniel will not long survive it. Since the war, various breeds of sporting dog have acquired favour and high prices, principally the spaniel, mahogany red, or spotted black and white, or liver and white. You may come across them on the sidewalk, always on a lead, with that look of rational despair that befits a sporting dog up on a visit to Paris. They are certainly sagacious, as they wait, eyes down, in the banana-queue at the fruiterer's. Sagacious they may be, yet they are gifted with a singular aptitude for getting lost. "*Lost, between Rue de Miromesnil and the Gare de l'Est, setter with collar but no address . . . Lost, Breton*

*spaniel answering to the name of Gamin . . . Lost,
spaniel . . ."* Who is to blame? On whom should my
suspicion fall? Alas, poor spaniel! Like Madame de
Sévigné, you find that to you the Paris pavement is a
place of torment, where the pads of your paws dry up
and crack, accustomed as they are to roam the marshlands
and hidden ditches where the veronica speedwell grows!
"Take the dog with you, you'll exercise him in the
course of your shopping!" And then all of a sudden there
is no dog, no lead, only the net-bag full of lettuces,
Toulouse sausages, and never quite ripe enough bananas,
that, and a poor lady deprived of her spaniel. *"Lost,
Market Lane Albert-Ier . . . Lost, Saint-Honoré Market
. . ."* Perhaps to the sensitive, chamois-leather nostrils
of the spaniel there came, somewhere between the stall of
rotting oranges and the gypseous cheese stall, a whiff of
Rambouillet from the water-cress crate, of spring water,
the scent of a young rabbit or a bird, the smell that puts
wings on a spaniel's paws and brings madness to his
highly trained narrow mind. *"Lost . . . Large reward
offered . . ."*

Spurned by fashion, what will now become of the pro-
lific cocker, with his eight-pup litters, black as Erebus?
His masters may love him, as often as not, for his own
sake, for his incurable sentimentality. His two main
worries are an atavistic nostalgia for the chase and any
chance remark he has half overheard, to which ever after
he attaches an unkind intention. He dwells on these con-
tinually and sheds secret tears. We do our best to console
him for the sake of his beautiful sad eyes. "Come here,
my precious darling, and let me pin back your lovely long
ears so that they won't get soaked in your food!" At least

he will never join the ranks of the forgotten schnautzer
with his gendarme's mustachios, or the bedlington with
his frizzy lamb's wool, who always reminds me, because
of the bump on his nose, of the late Duchess Sforza, *née*
Antokolski! But that is impertinence enough with regard
to the high and mighty persistent breeds, and Madame
Steinbock-Fermor will tell you better than I what points
to look for in a sleek bedlington.

The market for chestnut poodles is getting easier.
Trading in jet-black poodles shows signs of recovery. The
run on snow-white poodles is at a standstill. Little demand
for curly-haired poodles. It is worth noting that certain
poodle-fanciers remain faithful to the chestnut, to wit
Mlle Hilda Gélis-Didot and Francis Carco. M. Water-
mann still keeps to the jet-black breed. I purposely forgot
that one. I omit any mention of those clipped like topiary,
their sensitive bare backs exposed to the nip of rheumatics
and their bearded heads resembling Victor Hugo, or
Bébé Bérard.

The vogue for the boxer is at its height. No canine
character better deserves it, the bull-dog excepted. The
female has all the virtues, friendliness and mother-love,
and is so courageous in a fight that one fears for her life.
I speak from personal experience of one called Gertrude,
given us as a companion, short in the leg, fat as a sausage
because overfed, whose bright eyes spangled with grains
of gold dust earned her the nickname of "The lass with
the golden eyes". She knew how to hate as well as to
love, and would bare her teeth behind a curled back black
lip to rivals of every race. But to each member of our
family, hers by adoption, she meted out an impartial
affection amounting almost to an intoxicated vocal

display, for boxers sing and do everything but speak, and in this the cats were not excluded. O all you female boxers in your black masks creased with silky wrinkles! Here's a toast in your honour, and I don't mind saying that I am ready even now to be overcome with emotion when you go past me, leaving a trace of your short-haired racial odour, of warm ponies and clean-smelling breath! Your unforgettable way, entering body and soul into the family circle, there to sit and dream as you gaze at the fire, listening to the sound of voices, to thoughts, the last bang of the door closing, the overhead step on the ceiling!

Here, I think, is an *amende honorable* paid to the dog world. I have never boggled over them, but long experience has taught me that we are far too prone to excite the lyrical expression of a communicative dog. Three words in the special doggy tone of voice, a single pat, and a dog, quite unable to control his nerves, will break into his own language. "Get along with you," my mother would scold, "it will soon lead to tears." Handsome she was all the same, a sphinx with precious few secrets, as she sat there among us.

Her name was Gertrude. She used to sit on her creased haunches, like a naked woman, and dream as she stared into the fire. The life of an excitable dog is passing short.

That child, now, crying down there in the Garden, his mouth squarely open . . . He's been crying for some time. He puts me in mind of a Belgian child, who regularly started to cry at meal-times. Four to five years old, with lanky silken locks the colour of butter. In his relations with his weak-minded monther he always made use of the persistence which is the heritage of certain children, persistence on a scale to bring to the parent's face a sort of hunted look in which may be read the fleeting desire to see the death—to bring it about even!—of the child who is crying so shrilly. On one occasion this Belgian child, whose name was Jules, started to cry on sitting down at table and never left off. His soft-hearted mother did not send him packing, did not shut him up in the cellar or in the broom-cupboard.

He continued to bellow, with long-drawn, full-throated yells, while his mother, white as a sheet, said the first thing that came into her head. "Come, come, my pet . . . Jules, be quiet! A big boy like you, getting on for five! You won't get any whipped cream! If you don't shut up at once, Sir, you'll not go to mass—no, I mean the circus. My God, how miserable you make me feel! Why couldn't I have had a child who was dumb! Jules, I beg of you . . . Jules! obey your mother! "

Suddenly the child stopped short in the very midst of a bellow, whereupon the mother's face took on renewed colour and hope. She proceeded to give him crème Chantilly, gâteau de Savoie, dried plums, all of which he gobbled up. Next she treated him like a mother's little darling "was he feeling unhappy then! ", and wiped his eyes and mouth. At once Jules started bellowing again, louder and more incurably than ever. His mother stared at him, trembling before the mystery. "But why," she ventured to ask, "why are you crying again? "

He dried up for long enough to answer with composure, "I had not finished crying."

I have never understood it, never tolerated, never made vain use of this outpouring, this crying scandal, this square-mouthed grimace as in the act of being sick. With a sort of horror I view the quaking chin, the convulsive twitch at the corners of the lips, all the apparent signs of a cold in the head magnified twenty thousand times, the blackmail which is all that an access of sobbing amounts to. At the root of this horror of mine is the indignation shown by Sido at the wanton tears of children. Later in my life, I came across a feeling similar to my own in the ugly, providential old English paragon who looked after my daughter for seven years, and who used to say to her when only two and a half "Cry! Are you not ashamed to cry in front of me and in front of your mama? You should no more cry in front of anyone than do your business with the door open!"

In our intimate talks together Miss Draper would make profession of her faith. "Crying is a bad habit, that and no more. My baby doesn't cry when she falls down or has to go up to bed." The catalogue of her infant charge's virtues was interrupted only for the purpose of outlining for the same child a whole series of well deserved punishments. In times of juvenile rebellion and crisis, it was a never-failing satisfaction to me to mark on my daughter's rosy-cheeked face the battle waged with tears, the lip bitten in proud restraint, the struggle, begun so early, for self-control.

Once upon a time, however . . . On one special occasion I had to take my daughter up from La Corrèze to Paris and Miss Draper could hardly be said to have entrusted her to me with good grace. Bel-Gazou was five at the time, and with her fresh complexion and boy's knickers she enjoyed in Paris the success that was her due. For three full weeks, between the circus and the cinema, she never gave the least sign that to be parted from her Nursie-dear was an infliction. It is true that I saw her fetch one or two yawns and occasionally pull a long face, but I put all this down to her Paris diet. Also the suspicion that it might have something to do with the frivolous habits of her paternal grandmother, who wanted to teach Bel-Gazou the tango along with some other social amusements.

We set off on the return journey, the child and I, back to the Limousin fields speckled with cows, and small country houses perched on the tip-top of the little hills. On the train I introduced some subject of conversation which my daughter sifted for the purpose of acceptance or rejection in her usual calm if rather distant manner. As we approached Varetz I pointed out to her, in the setting of the landscape she knew so well, all the wonders she seemed to have forgotten, the osier-beds, the farmsteads, the winding Vézère, haunt of kingfishers. We had no carriage to meet us at the station, but the little toy-train would be putting us down not far from home. I looked out of the window before we drew up and caught sight on the platform of the tall, military figure of Miss Draper.

"Darling! Bel-Gazou! Look, there's 'Miss' waiting for us on the station! Now mind you say how d'you do to her nicely."

There was no question of her saying how d'you do nicely! I had beside me a small creature who had just burst into a flood of tears that were rolling down her velvet cheeks without wetting them. So shaken with emotion was she that she never dreamed of getting down from the train and could only sob " Nursie-dear, ooh-ooh-ooh! Nursie-dear! Nursie! "

There and then I learnt that a very small child can weep for joy in just the same way as a lovesick maid. As for Miss Draper! Never have I seen a gendarme at a country station weep so unashamedly, in full view of his half-section.

Before a moment was out, as we were crossing over the line, my daughter and her nurse were back in their usual state of estimable dissembling. My daughter was painting a vivid description of Paris, with an air of complete disdain for Le Long-Pré nestling among its flowers below her. Stiffly Nursie-dear was thrusting behind her all the seductive pleasures she had never experienced: " If you love Paris so much, you would do better to stay there. For my part, I've found it most peaceful here without you to plague the life out of me! "

The child down there in the Garden is still crying, but intermittently, now that his mother is gone. The enclosure being relatively free from dangers, children can be left there by themselves to learn about life, early and on their own, according to the codes of language and activity established during the last war. The crying ceases each time that the turning-out of a mud-pie (in the proportions of 50 per cent moist earth to 50 per cent droppings of various denominations) makes a call on the child's fingers. After that he starts whimpering again, but without real conviction. Another small boy now comes out from the shelter of the arcades, advances right up to the wire-netting round the lawn, lifts his head and shouts, as though summoning the pigeons, "Nah then, yer two muckers! 'Ave I ter come and take you by the . . ."

His shouts at once arouse a pretty little fair-haired girl, and a big curly-haired boy, who still stumbles as he walks. The trio move off. They are old acquaintances of mine, about whom I know almost all there is to be known, as you are now about to hear. Jojo, the eldest, is seven; he has reached the stage of his first year at school. A Paris street-urchin like so many others. Distinguishing marks: none. For cheek is not a distinguishing mark.

His sister, la Carrée, is four and a half. She is a pretty child, well filled-out, always with a cold hanging about her.

Their mother is a tired woman. Distinguishing marks: none. Tiredness is not a distinguishing mark in mothers with three children.

The Last, a boy of twenty-nine months.

Jojo, on coming home from school, hurls off his satchel with the authentic heave of the shoulders of an old salt.

"I've made it. I'm taken on."

His Mother: "Taken on? Taken on where? "

"Choir-boy. At Saint-Eustache."

"Since when? "

"I start—Sunday."

"You a choir-boy! I never heard such a thing! You're joking! "

"Joking! I'll say I'm joking! There's money in it—d'you get that! It pays. The pal who put me on to the fiddle has five hundred francs in his money-box already. Talk of a job! You fiddle a bit here, you fiddle a bit there. You say the mass. You fiddle a bit on that. I'm on to something, I tell you! "

"All the same, Jojo, you're not telling me that sort of thing can be fixed without the parents' consent! You're still under age—you can't go making your own agreements with curés! Even supposing your father . . . (*There follow many superfluous words that seem to have nothing to do with either Jojo, la Carrée, or the Last.*)

The following Sunday Jojo has a long lie abed, waiting his turn at the foot-bath.

His Mother (*with, for once, superior irony*): "Well, I thought you were going to mass?"

Jojo: "I've chucked it."

"Because why?"

"Because of the time, first. It's too early. And because of the métro. With the price they charge you for fares, I'd be lucky not to be out of pocket. I've given it a miss."

"And how about your tooth?"

"Still in. It moves a bit but it's still in. Look!"

"It's gone on for long enough. Tomorrow I'm taking you to the dentist."

"And what'll that cost you?"

"About two hundred, I don't doubt."

"Bit steep! (*Thinks*) M'man, will you pay me over the two hundred if I bring you the tooth tomorrow?"

"First bring me the tooth, then we'll see."

Jojo (*in the afternoon*). "There you are! (*He puts the small incisor into his mother's hand and then holds out his own.*) My two hundred?"

"Your two hundred! Two hundred francs to a child of your age? Two hundred francs, when a person such as me finds it hard enough to earn as much? I never heard such a thing!" (*Jojo howls. Interchange of loud cries.*

Jojo gets fifty francs. Appeasement. Momentary childishness.)

Jojo (in good humour): " Hi, la Carrée! What d'you say to a game of marbles? "

Voice of la Carrée: " No! It's raining in the garden."

Jojo: " We'll play on the landing. We'll make the pot in the hole left by the missing tile."

(*Silence. Enter la Carrée with blood on her mouth. She is crying, but making no fuss about it.*)

Jojo (interested): " What ever's the matter with you? "

La Carrée: " The bit of string cut me. I wanted to pull out a tooth with a bit of string."

Jojo: " Never knew you had one loose. Which tooth is it? "

La Carrée: " No, it's not loose. I wanted to touch fifty francs."

(*Explosion of cries in the next room. Maternal cries, and cries from the Last.*)

His Mother: " Now what's up with him? What's wrong with him? What a curse it is to have a child like that! Just take a look at him! His mouth all cut to pieces! To go and slash himself like that when he's only twenty-nine months old! What are children coming to these days, I ask you! "

La Carrée (aside to Jojo): " Don't let on. He's been trying to get a tooth out with the tin-opener. He wanted to touch fifty francs! "

Since December we have gone back to being ten at the Académie Goncourt. Lucien Descaves, however, a brisk octogenarian, is kept at home by his great age, a friend become fragile now and light as a vine-shoot. I have always enjoyed the Goncourt Lunches, even in the days of abstentions, frictions, and cleavages, when no more than five or six places would be laid. If there were not that little lift at Drouant's, I should certainly be rather cut off from my enjoyment; but then I could rely on the clasped hands of three or four men prepared to haul me up to the salon adorned by the flaky portrait of Edmond de Goncourt, and there I would settle down content. For we are a mixed company, fervent in our agreement to differ and wholly rebellious to the idea of unanimity. Dorgelès never misses an opportunity of going pop like a chestnut roasting on a brazier. Carco gets a fit of the sulks every now and again, when he relapses into silence and deprives us of the delightful timbre of his voice, that of a trained singer (the finest voice of any on the radio!). Larguier has the mischievous humour, and mane, of a playful lion, and roars in alexandrines. As for Billy? Billy knows everything that I do not know: that surely must make him the fountain-head of knowledge!

It is no good my posing as an old buck, for I still thoroughly enjoy the intensely feminine pleasure of being the only woman at the Goncourt Lunches, where I sit surrounded by a veritable Areopagus of men—five, six, eight, nine of them. And real men, worthy of the name—age does not enter into it—with all the faults and attractions of the male sex. Descaves has to be seen to be believed when he bangs on the table the size of a wheat-field, which destroys all confidence and intimacy, or when he submits the wines to the test of his nostrils or his tongue, or criticises the cooking; Rosny-jeune too, highly qualified to be present was a good sight, ruddy-cheeked

as an apple in autumn, his memory and hearing as sound
as ever for all his eighty-seven years! I perceive, and
derive comfort from the solicitude they do their best to
conceal. They have the air, one and all, of remembering
the woman I was once. From time to time our dashing
last-elect, Gérard Bauer, inscribes a "paper" to me in
words affectionate as a love-letter! I should like, as I
glance at the round table, to put on record that Arnoux
botanises like an angel gardener, and that Carco expounds
on the radio his novel method of writing history. But at
our meetings one person, and one person only, is subjected to our praise or dispraise, the candidate: we do
battle solely on behalf of outsiders. And I behave like the
others, as I sit among my male colleagues who bear the
outward signs of hard work, and often enough of weariness and ripe old age, and who, good men and true that
they are, lose their tempers, raise their voices, blaspheme.
Like any other human beings, they quarrel among themselves, but, thank heavens, they enjoy their food! Not one
among them has lost his zest for writing or his admiration
for authors. What else is there, other than this love and
devotion, to sustain us, year by year, along the hard
high road of the literature we have to read? For read we
do. We read a hundred to a hundred and twenty books.
We read novels of four hundred up to eight hundred
pages long. Once the time has come, we demolish, we
scatter to the four winds, the solid brick wall that has
lined my room. "Fortunately," say some of my friends
in a flippant and knowing tone of voice, "you don't need
to know their full contents, you can pick and choose at
will." No, that we cannot, even supposing we were so
minded. I tell you once again, we read. A strange assembly

indeed, that out of ten members numbers ten conscientious readers! Scrupulous, fallible, capable of making allowances for the still immature writer, of doing justice to youthful promise and living to regret it the following year! Does anyone imagine us to be reclining on a bed of roses when the bell rings for the last hour of the competitions? Our perplexities are summed up in a few faintly humorous lines for the evening papers: " With the help of the traditional oysters and the renowned *Blanc de Blanc*, all ten members of the Académie Goncourt are to be found gathered together at this time . . ." But no, no, things were not as gay as that when the time for the white wine and the casting of votes came along. Unanimous on Salacrou, but I could have wished for Anouilh too. Cheers for Hériat, but Miomandre has been too long forgotten. And then, why not Robert Kemp?

For me to feel happy, the Ten would have to be increased to twenty—at least.

This evening my room has the appearance of a robbers' cave: it is one of the days on which a jeweller neighbour of mine amuses himself, and amuses me still more, in pouring out over my table the contents of the velvet-lined case in which he carries round his latest treasures. Before my eyes is a gold clip, studded with sapphires. I can see a snail-shell embossed with turquoises in which has been reset a vivid though half-concealed little watch hardly bigger than a freckle. A heavy bracelet, most delicately wrought for its weight, has contrived to slip out to go and have a drink at my half-filled tumbler, as might a tame grass-snake. It is watched by the green eye of a chrysolite, a massive chrysolite ringed with brilliants, all that could be wished for to load a slender little finger and put the finishing touch to the mauve varnish of a convex nail.

Unguarded, an aquamarine pendant strays under my magic blue to replenish its own blue waters but these have been impounded with the thinnest network of tiny diamonds and enchained with gold. Thus it will have to wait, pendent, till it finds the more favourable shadows of the cleft between two breasts. Now where on earth has that heart-shaped tourmaline disappeared to? A moment since it was playing about with its all but wine-coloured pinks and reds between two turquoises. " Perhaps in the waste-paper-basket," my jeweller neighbour suggests, being a man of dry humour. The walls of my room are splashed with the dazzling glories of a Persian fairy tale as they catch the flashing sparkles from the unfathomable facets of the cut stones. That opaque contribution to the feast of colour—the turquoises—does something to assuage my own particular disorder. My friend and neighbour, the jeweller, assures me that the contemplation of precious stones brings relief to arthritic pains, that the majority of the gems snatched from the bowels of the earth are of beneficent effect. " Beneficent! What about the opal? " —" The opal too."—" But think of its reputation! Think of the well-attested instances when it has brought bad luck! " My neighbour shrugs his shoulders. "There have always existed clumsy folk who can't hammer in a nail without crushing their finger. They will always be with us. Take a particular look at this setting for a ring. I rather think it is my own invention. ' Knitted gold ', it is called. Do you like it? "

Its mesh is certainly fine enough to merit the name
"knitted"—or "netted", as we used to say in my part
of the country—each link atwinkle so that it appears
sprinkled with a fine sand of diamonds: definitely, I like
"knitted gold". What else is there that I like? This fat
chalcedony tortoise, smoky and star-spangled as the night
sky over Paris? No, I don't much care for it. It reminds
me of an idiotic craze for inlaying the shells of baby
tortoises while still alive. That dainty flowering spray of
beryls? I don't care for that either. It is too showy for
my taste. Let me have, rather, that bracelet of knotted
pliant cord, distinctive, oriental, a symbol of wealth and
respectability. I praise it unreservedly, I try it on. And
since, the Lord be praised, I can admire without coveting,
possess all without acquiring, I savour a pleasure which
itself is many-faceted, one which stems from a thoroughly
Parisian art, the fruit of inventiveness and patience,
requiring manual dexterity in a high degree . . . When
I dub my neighbour artisan, he blushes with the pride
of a man rewarded.

By improving my acquaintance with him, I am able
to increase my familiarity with an expansive taste in which
I have never indulged. I learn any number of names. I
finger the lovely yellow metal, cold at first but quickly
warming to the touch, the abettor of so many crimes and
wars. More than once, anticipating its eventual recipient,
have I held in my hands some gorgeous plaything long
promised and awaited with feverish impatience. In the
hollow of my hand I have held a precious stone, naked as
a slave without a master. I might well have believed it to
be a live ember I was smothering, so curiously did its
darting red and yellow fires glow within it. But my

neighbour shrugged his shoulders. "Pfui . . . that's a mere nothing. Even its name, a fanciful one at that, is of little account. There is not a single orange-coloured stone that is of value. If ever we break away from rubies, emeralds, and sapphires, or struggle to free ourselves from diamonds, we come back for all that to the diamond, the emerald, and the ruby. Or else we have to fall back on these other stones! "

These other stones I find charming, with names suggestive of liquid and transparent essences: the peridot, in which the bronze green always shows true, the varicoloured tourmaline, the easily accessible ruby spinel, the blue-green aquamarine, ever true to its name; and there is little danger of my forgetting you, my facetious chrysoberyl, green in the morning and turning red at night, such are the pleasing dissonances wrought in you by my blue lantern!

"Well, in that case, why do you not fall back on these other stones? "

But the master of the velvet-lined case showed little else but resignation as far as they were concerned.

"Pretty enough in their way," said he. "Amusing. I quite like using them as paving stones on cigarette-cases, as plaques on belts, as anything on a large scale. Up till now they have mistakenly been put to finicking uses. It would take more than our entire stock of ingenuity to give them what they lack . . ."

"And what may that be? My dear friend, you are on the verge of falling victim to the kind of snobbery that consists in reproaching them for their lack of hardness, popularity, rarity, consistency . . ."

He put a stop to my words by raising his hand, before he delivered a disconcerting monosyllable. "No," he said. "The real truth is that they lack the genuine look."

My evening visitors never fail me. Yesterday it was the small grey and green parrot with Maria Lydis. Last week I had that nice little woman, Madame Margat, and her female chameleon. Yes, my dear Miomandre, a female chameleon, just think of it! I doubt her long surviving her tiny mate, killed by our climate. She used to sleep in his arms, and he hugged her tight all the night long. Once bereft of her husband, she no longer wanted to go on living. After a few days she consented to eat a little, but her lustreless skin hung loose. The nice lady who brought her along to me set down her cage on my bench-table, beneath the blue lantern, and slowly, slowly, as if drawn by a magnet, the chameleon started to climb towards the source of light and heat. Once she had reached the roof of the cage, she again became quite motionless. We are always adepts at placing the right barrier, be it roof or wall, between an animal and liberty. Clinging tight by hands and tail to some leafy branches, the chameleon gradually assumed over the surface of her skin the varied harmony of their greens; meanwhile she kept flashing one or other of her eyes towards the lamp, so that they resembled a Directoire lorgnette in miniature.

I watch, I ask questions. I know so little about chameleons. But I had the presence of mind to refer Mme Margat to Francis de Miomandre, and that was something to the good. It was also good to learn from

Mme Margat that the small, lovely creature sometimes climbs to the top of a bottle and there reclines her chin on the cork. That in the evening she returns to her solitary abode among the leaves. That she sometimes instals herself in the fruit basket and puts her arm round a banana. That she licks the moist inside of a pear-peeling.

I do not always possess the courage and good sense to turn away from my door those whom I call my "evening visitors", be they birds, cats or dogs. They leave a wake behind them, the mark of creatures with whom I have exchanged credentials. I delight in nothing but their presence, and their departure drives me on to a growing sense of destitution, to a decision to forego the touch and sight of them, the coat, the paw, the deep-set eyes, the smile. My evening visitors normally make my time their own: they keep burning within me the persistent element of a flame, and of a dialogue. The Carcos' poodle (chestnut) deigns to endure boredom here from time to time. The poodle (chestnut) of Hilda Gélis-Didot is next in turn, but derives the same cold comfort. His name is Unic: he vents his impatience in huge sighs, looks at the time, deposits at the feet of his mistress a glove, a leash, a bag—all of them objects of a highly suggestive character. If Hilda pays no attention to them, Unic gives up, makes a melancholy meal off a detective story, or a sandal, or the small hearth brush. What a change is here from the worldly cheer of a parrot! Anatole-of-the-entresol sings, mimics to the best of his ability the bark of a watch-dog, the mewing of a cat, the human voice. And I would advise any burglar to keep away from his curved beak which can cut clean through a cutlet bone.

Yesterday evening the other parrot, the one belonging

to Mariette Lydis, took a strong dislike to his transport waggon when he had to reinstate himself in it. The bird is hardly bigger than a quail and dumb except for a very low cry. Back in his prison again, he took to demanding his immediate release by striking, time after time, three hard blows with his beak against the wooden side in perfect ryhthm: tock-tock-tock . . . tock-tock-tock. There is not a country in the world where prisoners and captives do not talk to each other in the language of tapping. But where had he learnt to count up to three, and even to three times three times three?

In this way there has been built up between animals and myself an understanding which has at times enriched and at others darkened my life. Each of my friends contributes something to it. From America I am sent cuttings from the illustrated papers in which I see that a bluish-grey cat is the model for baby linen de luxe and hats made to her size, that a dozen branches of the New York subway have been immobilised one after the other to allow the rescue of a fine tom-cat that had fallen into the cavity of a ventilation-shaft, that another tom-cat is able to open various locks and latches by a series of combined movements. But "Mimile" Blanchar is just as cunning without her picture ever having appeared in the papers. News from Bordeaux: a fine boxer bitch has just presented to the world a litter of eleven pups! (Madame Colette, what are we to do? They are all quite enchanting, but my bitch will soon be worn out. What advice can you give me?" Answered: "Buy good-milker-nanny-goat.")

News from elsewhere: "Madame Colette, I have at your disposal a pretty little sea-horse." I remember the proposals of Père Raux: "Wouldn't you care for a lovely lion-cub of four months? She sleeps on my bed." No, I do not want a pretty little sea-horse. Not even a tender octopus with great dreamy eyes, like the one that used to snuggle down caressingly into the hollowed hands of its keeper and friend at the Oceanographical Museum in Monaco. Above all, not an ape unjustly punished for its sins by looking like a sad little man!

A lonely little female chameleon; a Polish nightingale; a couple of parrots; a gentle, jovial boxer, Zorro Piguet, the colour of pig-skin, heavy as a tight-packed valise; the tiny pekingese, whose short life was entirely given over to the passionate worship of Germaine Fraysse; Crockie de Polignac, the golden basset-hound subject to nervous pregnancies—it is a short list, the list of my evening visitors. The Eden permitted us has nothing of a Noah's Ark about it.

The only living animal left to me that I can call my own is the fire. It is my guest, and the work of my hands. I know all about covering a fire, succouring a fire. I know the art of surrounding a fire in the open air with a circular trench, so that it may burn up well without "marking" the stubble and setting the ricks ablaze. I am well aware of its dislike of even numbers, that three logs burn better than two and seven than four, and that like every other animal it likes having its belly scratched from underneath.

Between it and me lies an old question which it takes me most of my time to resolve since it burns on my hearth for three-quarters of the year, there in my bedroom which has adopted its colours, red and white, and its presence. I burn it ceaselessly. Ceaselessly, but with a certain thriftiness. I pile it up, but with the air of doling out beggarly alms. I show it that I am a native of a distant province, where everyone learns not to waste wood and bread. I give it its quota of splinters, twigs and dried leaves, and I intend always to have the last word with it— that stand-by of trainers acquired through long dealings with animals. It repays me, by hurling itself upon the least of my offerings; it makes much of me, encourages me in my by now automatic incantations to it: the business of incantation loses nothing by it.

The hearth at which I solemnise my fire worship is of ancient construction and required, I don't mind betting, no more than the hand of a simple mason to build it. Within the precincts of the Palais-Royal we do have here and there some door-furniture and wainscot-panelling of artistic merit, along with a few fine fire-places. The marble has been stripped away from my own and replaced by a sort of pink and beige galantine. No matter, it has kept its intrinsic nature and its appetite for heat, together with that allegiance of permanent fixtures devised to share intimately in the life of man and his rudimentary needs.

Anyone who is given to meditating in front of a fire, during the hours when the shades of night beyond the window panes guarantee him safe protection, need no longer fear being joined at the fireside by the dog and the wolf of twilight—the shudder and the sudden start. Only novices in the art are liable at that time to be assailed so powerfully by age, fright, evil, or a guilty conscience. Let me run through my little incantation.

A fire affords such genial company
To the chill prisoner, the drear night long!
Close by my side there sits a good fairy
Who drinks, or smokes, or sings an ancient song . . .

Whose lines are those? I might almost go so far as to say they are my own, since once upon a time a competition for reading aloud was held in my canton for those of us who, when twelve or thirteen, were made to read with meaning and expression from both verse and prose. A certain well-intentioned man, having heard in our chief town that no child in the district had any conception how to read other than in a monotonous drone, was roused to indignation and, after pointing out the dire peril into which the ignorance prevailing in the department of Yonne could not fail to plunge the whole of France, founded an elocution prize. A red and gold volume, and a diploma, confirmed that at the age of twelve-and-a-half Gabrielle-Sidonie Colette knew how to read, and consoled me for having slurred my words while reading, so that I said " who drink sore smokes ", and inadvertently altered the prose of Madame de Sévigné.

A fire affords such genial company
To the chill prisoner . . .

Perhaps these second-rate verses really are mine. Mine as is the fire, as is everything that surrounds me at night.

Poetry does not necessarily have to be beautiful to stick in the depths of our memory, there to occupy most mischievously the place doomed to invasion by certain melodies which, however blameworthy, can never be expunged.

" A fire affords . . ."

Reading at night is a fickle ally. More reliable than a book is the setting I have arranged in honour of the

minutes and the hours. I am not always equal to my
bouts of insomnia, but I usually succeed in getting even
with them by the application of a sort of mental restora-
tive, which drives away fear of the unwonted from my
mind and my surroundings. It is not later than three
in the morning, nothing at roof-level is yet beginning
to pale. By reason of there being a lamp on every
pillar, I could count the number of arches along the
Palais-Royal from my bed. The inhabitants of this house
are so quiet that I never hear a soul at night; but the
clatter of my tongs into the grate would ruin the fitful
rest of even someone sleeping two doors away. Now, if
I am lying here motionless tonight, there is good reason
for it, for I can feel stirring within me—apart from
the twisting pain, as if under the heavy screw of a wine-
press—a far less constant turnscrew than pain, an insur-
rection of the spirit which in the course of my long life
I have often rejected, later outwitted, only to accept it in
the end, for writing leads only to writing. I am still going
to write; I say this in all humility. For me there is no
other destiny. But when does writing have an end? What
is the warning sign? A trembling of the hand? I used to
think that it was the same with the completed book as
with other finished ploys, you down tools and raise the
joyful cry "Finished!", then you clap your hands only
to find pouring from them grains of sand you believed
to be precious. That is the moment when, in the figures
inscribed by those grains of sand, you may read the
words "To be continued . . ."